Quality: Measuring and Monitoring

The Sunday Times 'Business Skills' series currently comprises books on total quality management, personal skills and leadership skills.

This first class series has received a warm welcome from readers and critics alike: the opinion of Christopher Lorenz of the *Financial Times*, for example, is that it is 'excellent ... well worth reading'. It is designed to build into an essential management library of authoritative and handsomely produced books. Each one, providing a definitive stand alone summary of best business theory and practice in its field, is also carefully co-ordinated to complement *The Sunday Times* 'Business Skills' video training package of the same name produced by Taylor Made Films.

BOOKS IN THE SERIES:

QUALITY: TOTAL CUSTOMER SERVICE
Lynda King Taylor
ISBN 0712698434

QUALITY: SUSTAINING CUSTOMER SERVICE
Lynda King Taylor
ISBN 0712655190 (P)

QUALITY: ACHIEVING EXCELLENCE
Edgar Wille
ISBN 0712698639

QUALITY: CHANGE THROUGH TEAMWORK
Rani Chaudhry-Lawton, Richard Lawton, Karen Murphy, Angela Terry
ISBN 0712698337

EFFECTIVE MEETINGS
Phil Hodgson, Jane Hodgson
ISBN 0712698736

TIME MANAGEMENT
Martin Scott
ISBN 0712698531

SUCCESSFUL PRESENTATIONS
Carole McKenzie
ISBN 071265691X (P)

LEADERSHIP: THE ART OF DELEGATION
David Oates
ISBN 071265610 (P)

LEADERSHIP: THE ART OF MOTIVATION
Nick Thordy and Dan Lees
ISBN 071265464 (P)

Quality: Measuring and Monitoring

by

Tony Bendell, John Kelly, Ted Merry

and Fraser Sims

CENTURY
BUSINESS

First published in the UK 1993
by Century Business
An imprint of Random House UK Ltd
20 Vauxhall Bridge Road, London SW1V 2SA

Random House Australia (Pty) Ltd
20 Alfred Street, Milsons Point
Sydney, NSW 2061, Australia

Random House New Zealand Ltd
18 Poland Road, Glenfield
Auckland 10, New Zealand

Random House South Africa (Pty) Ltd
PO Box 337, Bergvlei, South Africa

Set in Bembo by SX Composing Ltd, Rayleigh, Essex
Printed and bound in Great Britain by Mackays of Chatham PLC, Kent

British Library Cataloguing in Publication Data
A catalogue record for this book is available from the British Library.

ISBN 0-7126-5514-X

Contents

Acknowledgements

The authors are grateful to the many people and organisations who have contributed to the case studies in this book.

In particular, we would like to acknowledge the hospitality, patience and general helpfulness demonstrated, and the time and effort committed by the undermentioned:

John Hughes, Works Manager of Triplex Safety Glass Company Limited in Kings Norton and his Senior Management team, for material on the Cost of Quality in chapter 4; Bert Vermeulan, Quality Manager of Hewlett-Packard's Computer Peripherals Bristol Division, for material on Critical Success Factors (CSFs) in chapter 5; Fred Attwood, Product Quality Executive of Marconi Defence Systems Limited in Portsmouth, for CSFs material in chapter 5 and Statistical Process Control (SPC) material in chapter 10; East Midlands Electricity, and specifically Roger Davis of the Quality Development Department, who proof-read it, for the material related to CSFs in chapter 5; Terry Lyons, Quality Executive of Meritina, Coats Viyella Apparel CMT Division at Mansfield, for the Process Development Flowchart in chapter 6; Ray S Robertson, Manager, Operations Programme Management of NCR (Manufacturing) Limited in Dundee, for case study material on benchmarking in chapter 7; Claus Møller, Time Manager International A/S, for permission to use figures 92-94 in chapter 9; Peter Holman, Quality Consultant of TSB Bank plc in Birmingham, for case studies on SPC used within chapter 10; Paul Holmes, Site Advisor on MDQ and Terry Twine, Advisory Statistician for the Quality & Product Assurance Dept. of IBM Havant for material on the application of Taguchi methodology in chapter 10; Roy Peacock of the European Foundation for Quality Management, for material on The European Quality Award in chapter 11; Ian Raisbeck, Quality Director, Royal Mail and George Rendall, Quality Support Manager, Royal Mail London, for the case study which comprises chapter 12.

We also wish to acknowledge the help and support of many others who have contributed to this work.

Tony Bendell
John Kelly
Ted Merry
Fraser Sims
29 July 1992

1. Quality Management and Pursuit of Excellence

1.1 THE IMPORTANCE OF QUALITY

There is little doubt that Quality has become the by-word of the 1990s. Advertisements, high street stores, and even lorries broadcast that a particular organisation or business, and its products, are quality orientated. Quality has become a strategic issue, with many Annual Reports of major companies making strong references to the initiatives they have undertaken and the concern they have demonstrated in achieving it.

However, whether such organisations truly understand the real meaning of Total Quality is open to question. One dilemma of current commercial life is that quality means different things to different people, from the performance of a specific product or service offered to the consumer, to the way the entire organisation is managed.

Quality of the product has always been of importance, from the Ancient Egyptian era to the present day. The pre-industrial revolution craftsman often had the advantage of being the owner, sole operator and salesman, and as such was able to assess the needs and requirement of the customer at first hand, subsequently modifying the product and process accordingly. Standards existed in the form of Craft Guilds to protect the business area from inadequate, or unskilled, interlopers.

A consequence of the Industrial Revolution was that as businesses became larger, the owner and the customer became more separated, whilst the 'craftsmen' or operators became merely a part of the process as an extension of the machines.

The perceived change in the role of those working within the business was compounded, to some extent, by the work of F.W. Taylor. In order to compensate for a shortage of skilled labour in the United States, and overcome the language and educational barriers amongst the large immigrant population, work was deskilled by breaking down the process into discrete, simple elements which could be performed routinely by the operator.

These routines were developed into measured standards, and so the basis for regarding the operator as merely an extension of the machine had been laid.

It is not too long ago that a sign outside many factories read 'Hands Wanted'. This could have been (rightly?) interpreted as 'leave your brains at the factory gates – we just want your hands'.

However, perhaps the current high profile of quality has its origins in the Far East after the defeat of Japan in the Second World War. Concerned with ensuring effective supplies to the military, and rebuilding the Japanese economy, the Americans needed to ensure that the quality of products leaving Japan was of much the same standard as those in the West. At that time, the post–war boom was creating a situation in which the consumer, long starved of commodities, never mind luxuries, would buy most items offered for sale. It was a production led market.

It was at this stage that the Americans made what was probably one of the greatest mistakes in their history – they encouraged the development of SPC in Japanese industry.

A key player in the Japanese development of quality was Dr W. Edwards Deming. Dr Deming had originally gone to Japan to advise the Japanese Census.

Whilst working in Japan, he became involved with the newly formed Union of Japanese Scientists and Engineers (JUSE). Subsequently, as Deming became more widely known, JUSE invited him to lecture on statistical methods. By 1960, Deming and his teachings were widely known in Japan, and the Emperor awarded him the Second Order of the Sacred Treasure.

Deming's message to the Japanese was basically a statistical one. However, his approach included non–manufacturing and human variation, in addition to manufacturing variability. He taught managers to study variability, and to understand the difference between common causes and special causes, the latter being the type of variation which prevents performance from being consistent in a statistical sense.

Deming believed that managers who did not understand variation, and confused the two types, could make matters worse. However, Deming's message extended some way beyond statistical methods, and he encouraged the Japanese to adopt a systematic approach to problem solving which became known as the Deming or PDCA (Plan, Do, Check, Action) cycle.

Dr Edwards Deming was followed to Japan by Dr Joseph Juran, a Balkan born American. Like Deming, Juran was invited to Japan in the early 1950s by JUSE, and subsequently conducted seminars for top and middle level executives. His lectures emphasised the managerial aspects of quality and focused on planning, organisational issues, management's responsibility for quality and the need to set targets and goals for improvement.

Of the many aspects of Juran's message on quality, the belief that quality does not happen by accident, but must be planned, was fundamental.

Deming and Juran may be regarded as the fathers of the quality revolution, and intrinsic in their messages is the concept of *measurement* for both control and improvement planning purposes.

So it was that the Japanese learnt not only how to equal, but how to surpass and overtake Western product quality standards. They had discovered, and learned, a *process* for improvement of quality. Having equalled Western quality, they did not stop but continued to examine their processes and products in order to seek further improvements, as illustrated in Figure 1.1.

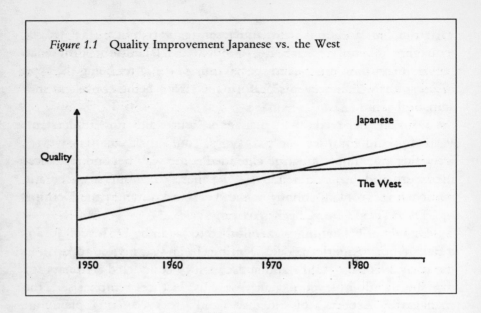

Figure 1.1 Quality Improvement Japanese vs. the West

1.2 QUALITY MANAGEMENT/TQM VERSUS PRODUCT OR SERVICE QUALITY

A major barrier is the understanding of the meaning of the word quality. Whilst the word is used regularly to describe products, and we see advertising for 'quality carpets', 'quality double glazing' and so on, it can, and often does, cause confusion since individual perceptions of what quality is will vary. In particular, in organisations, there is a clear need to understand what quality is, since exhortations to 'make quality products' will be interpreted in different ways by different people.

The word quality has often been used to denote a degree of excellence, for example, in a painting, a Sassoon hairstyle or a Rolls Royce car. However, this is a very imprecise and nebulous concept, and is of little use within the manufacturing or service organisation.

One useful definition of quality is 'meeting the requirements of the customer'. It should be noted that requirements may also include criteria of price, or delivery, in addition to the specific performance of the product or service itself. Consequently, it becomes evident that the first step is to define those requirements by asking the customer. This may be achieved by direct discussion, surveys or observations on purchasing behaviour. Using this definition of quality, then if the requirements are for a car which is economical to run, and easy to park in central London, then a Rolls Royce may not be a quality car.

Requirements have often been set upon the basis of a specification, and quality has sometimes been defined as 'conformance to specification'. This definition contains key elements which are essential for the effective measurement and monitoring of quality, because a specification should be drawn up based on an assessment of the requirements of the customer and the capability of the organisation to produce or deliver. Once the specification has been established, quality is interpreted as a matter of ensuring that the specification has been met.

However, there are serious weaknesses in a definition based on conformance to specification. First of all, it sets a level which can be considered satisfactory, and does not take into account the changing needs and requirements of the customer. Secondly, it can over-emphasise the inspection aspects of the process, which aims to ensure that nothing is delivered to the customer which does not meet the demands of the specification. It leads to the very harmful psychological effect of setting limits beyond which quality does not need to be improved.

From very early usage, Total Quality Management (TQM) has meant different things to different people. Some organisations have treated it purely as a motivation campaign, to improve service to external and internal customers.

Others have recognised that beyond training, teamwork and the use of statistical tools, there is in Total Quality Management the quest for the self improving organisation. In this quest, cultural change, organisational change, the use of simple tools and a documented quality management system all have a part to play.

Figure 1.2   Possible organisational Issues

No clear relationship with customers
No awareness of cost of quality
Suspect workforce are under-utilised
No real measurement of staff performance
Need to understand the real purpose of the group
No clear picture of total rework
No description of output quality
Redundant procedures need updating
No standard operating model for the department
Difficulty in identifying internal improvement areas

Some of the issues that may be apparent in an organisation are shown in Figure 1.2. These are subtle deficiencies that go beyond conventional definitions of product or service Quality Assurance. Resolving these is what TQM is about.

Some of the basic principles of TQM are shown in Figure 1.3.

Figure 1.3   Basic principles of TQM

Fundamental *cultural shift* from Quality Assurance, Quality Control
Theme of *Continuous Improvement*
Customer orientated (Internal and external)
"Right first time" standard
Everybody in the company involved
Led by senior management
Measure *Quality Costs*
Prevention philosophy
Supported by *Quality Management System*

A self improving organisation is one in which the rest position is improvement; one in which if you never did anything else to the organisation again it would carry on improving. Figure 1.4 illustrates this concept of a TQM organisation.

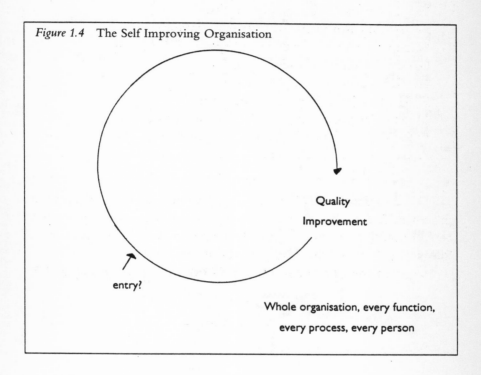

Figure 1.4 The Self Improving Organisation

Quality

Improvement

entry?

Whole organisation, every function, every process, every person

The problem is how to break into the self improvement cycle?

1.3 WHY AIM FOR EXCELLENCE IN CUSTOMER SATISFACTION?

It is vitally important to the success of any organisation to understand what the end–customer or consumer wants, to define clearly those requirements and to find a means of measuring them. What is seen as important by the end–customer, may be different from the concerns of the supplier.

The post-war boom years, when most companies could 'make it and ship it out', have come to an end. Many markets have become saturated and product or service differentiation become less marked. The emergence of the Pacific Basin countries as world suppliers has increased competition worldwide, and the rapid progress in communications and transport together with the lowering of national barriers within Europe, has led to labour, materials and information being more readily available. Businesses have come to realise that it is the way in which the internal processes of the organisation are put together which can give them a competitive edge. They need to improve continuously in order to satisfy, and if possible delight, the customer, who is in a position to choose from a plethora of available products and services.

1.4 HOW TO IMPROVE – CLEAR THOUGHT AND DIRECTION

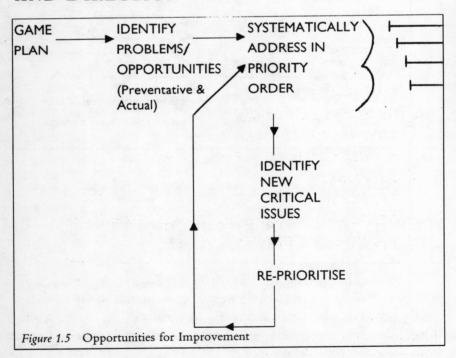

Figure 1.5 Opportunities for Improvement

In theory it is simple – all we need to do is construct a plan, identify problems and opportunities for improvement and systematically address these in priority order, re-prioritising as the need arises. (See Figure 1.5.)

In starting to execute this plan, different critical issues will be of importance to different organisations. The ones shown in Figure 1.6 correspond to those identified by a small manufacturing company, but there is surprising commonality in many organisations. Initial vision building with top management to clarify where the organisation is going and to enable meaningful objectives and targets to be set is often essential. Communications problems and nearness to the 'voice of the customer' also usually need to be tackled.

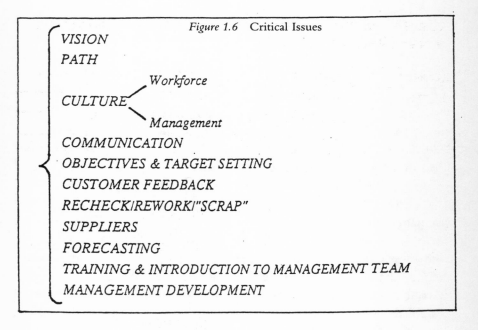

Figure 1.6   Critical Issues

VISION
PATH
                    Workforce
CULTURE
                    Management
COMMUNICATION
OBJECTIVES & TARGET SETTING
CUSTOMER FEEDBACK
RECHECK/REWORK/"SCRAP"
SUPPLIERS
FORECASTING
TRAINING & INTRODUCTION TO MANAGEMENT TEAM
MANAGEMENT DEVELOPMENT

There are essentially three stages to the path of TQM, as illustrated in Figure 1.7. A crucial stage, often neglected, is to start by finding out where you are now.

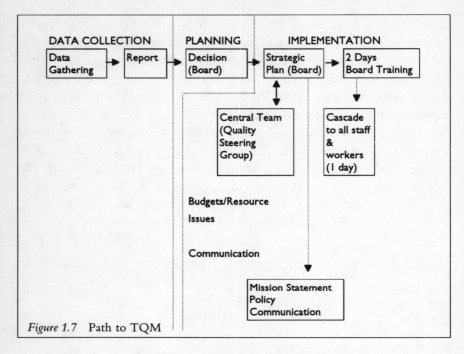

Figure 1.7   Path to TQM

Initial data collection, including anonymous questionnaires and independent interviews with members of the workforce, as well as Heads of Function, is essential to identify gaps in practices, poor communication, inadequate management, how people work around problems and how these problems could be avoided.

Only when this data collection stage is complete can top management plan implementation. Typically this will be with the help of consultants who have undertaken the data collection, working with the board in workshop sessions. A good way forward at the start of the implementation stage is for a small Quality Steering Group, preferably chaired by the Managing Director, to be established to manage the path to TQM. It will decide resources, monitor, facilitate and remove barriers to progress. Basic awareness training is now necessary and the board needs to commit itself long-term by issuing a mission statement to tell the employees, customers, suppliers and possible other 'stakeholders' the path forward. Experience suggests that a 'cascade' model of training rather than a 'wall to wall' training is to be preferred for TQM awareness.

Figure 1.8 illustrates, for a one-site company of perhaps 100 employees, the way a TQM programme might be implemented. The activities shown above the line should take place within every department; those below the line are cross-departmental. It is crucial for the organisation to incorporate quality improvement into its normal management processes as soon as feasible, rather than keeping quality improvement separate from the 'real work'.

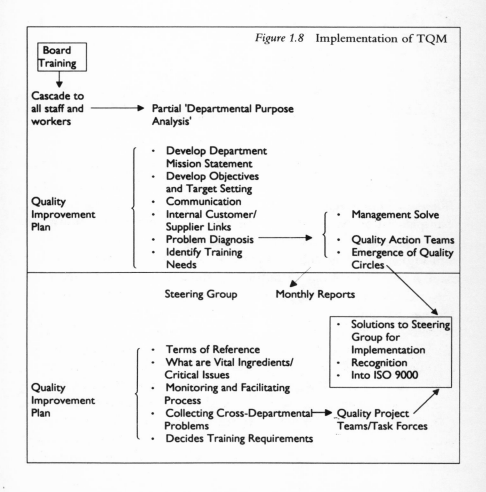

Figure 1.8 Implementation of TQM

It is also crucial to remember that the path to TQM requires mass education, a team based philosophy and the use of simple tools. All are necessary; one alone is not enough, as shown in Figure 1.9.

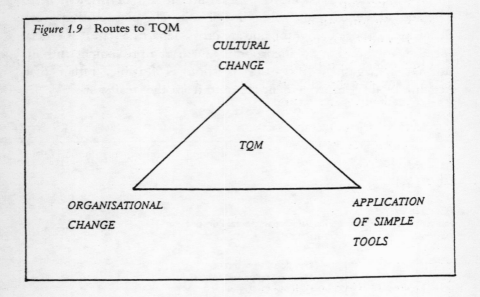

Figure 1.9 Routes to TQM

CULTURAL
CHANGE

TQM

ORGANISATIONAL
CHANGE

APPLICATION
OF SIMPLE
TOOLS

What Can Go Wrong?

The path to TQM is a long-term activity. Most organisations will quote three to five years. Some such as Motorola and Florida Power and Light who have achieved enormous success may quote ten.

There are many opportunities for things to go wrong. Some of the most common dangers and common mistakes are shown in Figures 1.10 and 1.11.

Figure 1.10   Common Dangers

Too Complex Tools
  Ownership
  Communication
  Resources/time/overload

Individual Not Team
  Lack of cohesion   Barriers
  Inadequate evaluation

Lack of Programme Cohesion
  Team lack of focus
  Overload

Figure 1.11   Common Mistakes

TQM = Trainings (and teams)
Weak/infrequent steering committee
Lack of management to programme
No measurement/historical measurement/lack of customer focused measurement
Part-time facilitators/no direct reporting
Inadequate 'how to' training
'Tools-only' training with no support
No monitoring/lack of support to teams
Competing unco-ordinated programmes
Improvements only by teams/only big improvements
TQM = Customer care

Organisational requirements and training requirements to do it correctly are shown in Figures 1.12 and 1.13.

Figure 1.12   Organisational Requirements to do it Correctly

ORGANISATIONAL REQUIREMENTS

Steering Committee
   Senior/decision makers/resources
   Strong
   Regular/frequently
   Monitoring/measuring/reviewing
   Approving/recognising
   Steering

Facilitators
   Full time
   Direct reporting to MD
   Trained
   Mentors/trainers
   Eyes and ears
   Do not solve
   Obstacle removers

Teams
   Clear terms of reference
   Approved projects/implement
   Trained
   Clear reporting line for team upwards
   Supported

Complete Integrated Programme

Figure 1.13   Training Requirements

Awareness Training
    Cascade
    Deploy policy

TQM Role Training
    Programme manager
    Steering committee
    Facilitators
    Team leaders

Tools Training
    Team members
    Managers
    Quality circles

Mentoring/Training/Self Development

How Should You Start?

Do not rush in; at least tentatively plan the whole programme before commencing awareness training or issuing a mission statement. If at all possible, obtain suitably qualified help. But avoid 'ready made' packaged solutions. Total Quality Management needs to be purpose built by you, with qualified help for your organisation.

1.5 A REVOLUTION IN INTERNAL BUSINESS PROCESSES

Total Quality Management is a strategic approach aimed at producing the best product or service currently available through innovation and continual improvement. It is recognising that each person within the organisation is – or should be – the expert within their particular role or function, and it is that person who has, very often, first hand knowledge of their part of the process and therefore ideas on how to improve it.

As mentioned earlier, some organisations have treated Total Quality Management purely as a motivational campaign. We have all seen posters around the walls exhorting employees to 'Get it right first time'. Whilst this objective is highly commendable, it can often appear as an insult to someone who has worked there for ten years, and has, as far as he or she is aware, been getting it right first time. The problem normally is that we have not all, by discussion, agreed what the 'it' is we are trying to get 'right first time'.

This leads to a rather hit and miss type of operation where the only way of protecting the customer from defective products or poor service is to put a great deal of emphasis on end-point inspection, which anyway is unreliable. However, the difficulty with this approach is that it takes place when the product or service is at its most expensive, that is, when all the work is complete. In addition, it is also the most critical time to ascertain whether the end product is good enough or not, because the next stage is delivery to the customer, and failure of product will usually mean failure to deliver. It is essential to realise that quality cannot be inspected in, but must be designed and manufactured into, the product or service. Increasing the end line inspectors ten-fold will not improve the manufactured quality of the 'product', it will just reduce the chances of the customer receiving defectives.

To many employed within the organisation, demands to 'meet the requirements of the customers' can seem irrelevant. After all, perhaps only a small percentage of all employees will ever meet end customers face to face, so how can they understand and interpret their needs?

Whether a secretary, operator, or an accounts clerk, each individual has a role to play in improving quality, but often fails to realise it because they are distanced from the customer. This is also true in the service sector, where staff employed in clerical, administrative and supervisory positions within banking, the Health Service or local authorities could all interpret the customer as merely someone who receives the end product or service.

It is very helpful, therefore, if everyone within the organisation regards themselves as both an internal customer and an internal supplier. The internal customer is the next person, or department, in line, because every day they depend upon the work, information, decisions or resources provided. Likewise, there are internal suppliers, i.e. those people within the organisation who supply all that is necessary for the work to be carried out at the next stage. If there is a breakdown between customer and supplier, then the quality of the end product or service will be less satisfactory, as shown in Figure 1.14.

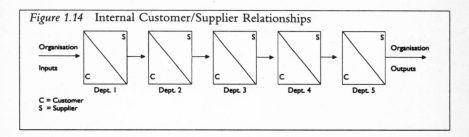

Figure 1.14   Internal Customer/Supplier Relationships

1.6 KEEP IT SIMPLE, KEEP IT VISIBLE

Some time ago, we held a workshop on Total Quality Management and the approaches which might be used for its effective implementation. At the end of the proceedings, each delegate was asked individually for his views on what he had heard. One senior manager confirmed that the workshop had been enjoyable and informative but expressed the view that it was all rather simple in its concepts. When asked whether his company applied the principles, he said, '*Oh no, we don't do it!*'

It has been said that Total Quality Management is common sense applied in an uncommon way. This may well be true, but the difficulties which can be encountered in effective implementation are considerable. It is essential therefore, that at all stages of Total Quality Management implementation there are clear statements to everyone within the organisation about:

1. What we are aiming for
2. Where are we now.

Too often, companies have issued Mission Statements or a Quality Policy which is very general, and unquantified. For example, to *'become the best'* is a well intentioned aim, and is very difficult to argue with. However, the next step should be to define the best, and to measure and monitor progress towards it. Unless such statements are interpreted to demonstrate to each employee what he or she needs to achieve, and they are able to measure their progress towards those goals, little is likely to change.

2. The Meaningful and the Mundane – Why and How Measurement Matters

2.1 BREAKING OUR CURRENT VIEW OF MEASUREMENT

The theme of this book is that measurement of internal business procedures is crucial to achieving excellence in customer satisfaction. Unfortunately, however, this has often not been clearly understood by management or has been implemented very wrongly. In this book, we attempt to show the need for measurements of quality, the nature of such measurements, how business processes should be identified and monitored and how measurement thus attained should be used in planning, steering and achieving quality as part of Total Quality Management. This book treats issues of measurement in the broadest sense including the use of benchmarking as the basis for comparison and targeting, as well as the human aspects of measurement in customer perception and personal quality.

There is general agreement that some form of measurement is essential to achieve excellence in customer satisfaction. However, such measurement is regarded as a boring subject and typically badly applied. Often in the past measurement has been carried out for its own sake. Whilst correctly applied measurement is an essential part of focusing improvement programmes, the sort of measurements actually applied and to what and how they are used, are crucial.

Why is measurement of quality, in particular, a difficult subject? The question has lots of dimensions. It is hard to believe that anyone would implement measurement for its own sake without having a clear purpose for the results of the measurement process, but in many senses this has happened in quality.

Why does it occur? One reason is that measurements on *inputs* are often provided to demonstrate the level of commitment, effort and resource going into a quality improvement programme – 'bums on seats' is a classic example of this misconception of the value of measurement. So too is the counting of the number of quality improvement teams. Another example is bureaucratic measurement of internal processes carried out, for example, in organisations historically in the public sector but now perhaps moving into the private one. Masses of data of an historic nature, not related to customer requirements and used for historical reporting rather than for control or monitoring, are typical characteristics of this type of measurement. So too are the large database empires often feeding off such situations. These, in turn, give rise to desires for further measurement to protect the empire. The lack of flexibility of the system on which they are built, however, typically makes the data they contain of extremely limited value.

What is really needed is a unified measurement system to be used for planning, for monitoring and for driving improvement. Chapters 4 and 5 of this book describe two unified measurement approaches which can be utilised to this end.

These are the **Cost of Quality** approach, which has been a fairly common unifying method in the United Kingdom, and the less applied **Critical Success Factor** approach. Whatever method is used it is crucial to avoid a plethora of individual, uncoordinated measurements which point us in different directions and make it difficult to prioritise and to unify and conceptualise the overall situation. The key to successful measurement systems is *simplicity* both in the nature of individual measures and in the method of unification into a coherent, clearly structured system.

This view of a simple unified approach to measurement, however, is diametrically opposed to the views of some quality and statistical specialists who have purposely attempted to develop and protect the application of measurement as a specialised subject with great complexity, jargon and intellectual content. The concentration on technical complexity and advanced techniques has taken precedence over the mass use of unifying systems which can be understood by all. *Why does this occur?* It is partly ignorance, it is partly the result of academic statistical training and education; and it is partly the lack of planning on the role of tools. The result is, typically, that we drown in data, data is so complicated that it is irrelevant to decision making, and measurement is seen by managers as limited and is not applied.

Measurement must be seen as an integral part of a planned, implemented quality management programme. Selection of key measures must be part of senior management's responsibility and they must be collectively identified, agreed, monitored and used as the basis for decision making. We consider how this is done in Chapters 4 and 5.

Measurement today, however, is such an unsavoury subject for those interested in quality that the title of this book has been deliberately constructed to avoid the possible connotations of a shorter more conventional title such as Quality Measurement. This book is not full of equations or complicated measurement techniques. *Measurement is neither boring nor complex; it is essential in the process of monitoring internal business processes to ensure excellence in customer satisfaction.*

2.2 PAST DISASTERS – HOW WE USED MEASUREMENT WRONGLY

Whilst the incorrect use of measurement has its origins in the educational system, its existence is plainly evident in all factories and in the management processes of our organisations. A coherent view of measurement is uniquely absent in almost all major western organisations, the one exception being the measurement of money, since the pursuit of profit and the minimisation of cost have long been objectives of top priority for western management. Financial reporting systems have caused us to look at such crucial measurements on a historic basis and the systems have emphasised output measures, such as profit, and input measures, such as cost, but not internal process measures.

With this naive approach to measurement, it was only a small extension to emphasise productivity, but not quality. The causal relationships that link quality and quality management to profitability are far from clear, and are subject to external disturbances, as well as other internal management decisions and processes. In this process of extension, then, quality measures were neglected.

The exceptions were quality measures that had a direct relevance to profit through the medium of productivity. Defective products occurring in manufacturing are a prime example. However, even in this area the concept of measurement was reactive; the implicit assumption being that the production process would work and produce perfect items, but when this was not realised, inspection and monitoring were required. Defective items were identified for rectification and records were kept of their incidence because of the impact on cost.

In sophisticated companies, statistical process control systems (SPC) were introduced, but alas, very often without the necessary preparatory work. Control charts were built for product attributes rather than process variables, so that effective control of the process by adjusting process conditions in order to prevent defects before they occur, was not possible. Also, very often no experimentation or analysis was undertaken to identify correctly the appropriate process variables or product features that should be controlled. Thus irrelevant variables, or too many variables were incorporated into the, so-called, SPC system. Automatic measuring equipment connected to software systems exacerbated this situation, throwing out literally dozens of control charts at a frequency too great for the operators to cope with. Nor could they respond quickly enough to control their process.

This naive idea of measurement was almost entirely restricted to production areas. However, measurement was also used in other parts of the organisation, primarily in the study of variables which were believed to have a direct causal link to profitability. For example, market surveys were used to understand customer perceptions and buying habits in mass consumer markets.

What was lacking was a unified approach, which looked at the organisation and its performance in terms of what it was trying to achieve. It is true to say that some steps in this direction were introduced by Customer Care programmes. Even the naive identification of factors that were thought to matter to the customer and their linking back into the activities of front-line staff went some way to clarify the potential for measurement as a unifying tool within the organisation. The classic 'answer the phone in three rings' criterion, whilst frequently resulting in transferred calls and dissatisfied customers left to wait, represented the introduction of measurement in internal business processes in an attempt to achieve customer satisfaction. The measurements were not always appropriate, the targets were often badly set, more important measures and criteria were often neglected, but meaningful measurement was introduced where it had not been before and in a way that was more than just work study.

With the introduction of Total Quality Management programmes it might have been expected that a fundamental new approach to the measurement process would be introduced. This was not so. Legitimately the path to Total Quality Management can be said to incorporate cultural change, organisational change and the application of simple tools. Many UK and western programmes have concentrated exclusively on the cultural change aspect, while others have been concerned with the introduction of procedures and discipline in the context of ISO 9000/BS 5750. Those that have concentrated fully or partly on the application of simple tools, have often applied them in a marginal segregated way and rarely, if ever, as a fundamental driving force within a Total Quality Management initiative. There are exceptions; the Motorola Six Sigma programme, now copied by many organisations, focuses on the continuous reduction of variation over time within the organisation. However, most frequently this has once again been applied to the manufacturing processes exclusively, with little or no attention to the non-manufacturing business processes throughout the rest of the organisation. Measurement is restricted to the manufacturing stages requiring improvement.

There have been champions inside our organisations who have wanted us to measure. But whilst it is always a good principle, they were frequently not too sure about the detail of exactly what and why. Measurement often became entrenched. Historic and obtusely relevant information was made available as (potentially) the basis for decisions. The right measurements were perhaps not available for decision making, whether in the executive suite, on the shop-floor, or in the board room. Worst of all, however, people have been unclear about their purposes. There is no point in measuring until you know what you're trying to achieve.

2.3 HOW DOES MEASUREMENT RELATE TO EXCELLENCE IN CUSTOMER SATISFACTION?

There are many views as to the purposes of organisations; they exist to make money for the shareholders, they exist to provide employment for their workforce, they exist to serve the community, they can even be seen as existing to provide a market for the products their suppliers supply. All of these, and other, stakeholders have an interest in the future and the wellbeing of the organisation. Which group or groups are seen as being of predominant interest, depends upon the political and social system, the financial and organisational background to the organisation, economic circumstances and the view of the management team within the organisation. In recent years interest has focused on **the customer** as a simple, unifying approach in the pursuit of organisation excellence. For private organisations, at least in the short term, the customer is king. The private enterprise organisation needs to satisfy the customer requirement to retain customer loyalty and to extend its market share in the face of increasing world competition, removal of trade barriers and the quest for improved efficiency. Within commercial organisations the importance of the customer has become paramount.

In public sector and public service organisations, emphasis on the customer has enabled the organisation to revitalise its focus on its reason for existence. In these circumstances, the customer is often ambiguously defined. One of the problems of TQM in the public service sector is that there are often multiple customers within the same transaction. For example, when a policeman arrests a criminal his customers include the criminal, the victim, the community including perhaps ethnic minorities, the Home Office to whom he provides statistics, the legal system etc. Similarly, is the customer of higher education the student, the employer, the government or the schools who provide the input? Whilst the debate is an important one to enable public service organisations to focus on meeting the needs and desires of all the customer groups, there is now little debate about the fact that they exist to serve customers.

If our organisations exist to serve customers and their commercial – and for public service organisations political – future depends upon the satisfactory discharge of this responsibility, then it is clearly a legitimate management target to pursue excellence in customer satisfaction. *How can this be achieved?* A quote by the father of the Japanese quality revolution, Edwards Deming, comes to mind. 'Everyone doing their best is not the answer, it is first necessary for people to know what to do.'

What to do here is to identify what really matters to our customers and how we can provide an excellent service in respect of it. The definition of excellence comes from the customers, from our own internal evaluation of its meaning and from the activities and philosophies of our competitors. We need **targets** and we need to **benchmark** our progress and our targets against those of competitors and of world best practice; we should not concentrate on just measuring our products or core services. Frequently, we find that it is not the product itself which matters to our customer, nor the core service, but the bundle of characteristics that we provide around it – maintenance, repair, advisory services, presentation, the delivery system – all have a part to play in the aspects of excellence as perceived by our customers. Once we have obtained consensus on what matters, we must establish a time-based target, put plans into being for reaching the targeted levels of performance, monitor our progress towards this, monitor our competitor's best practice and react when we have fallen behind.

To monitor, to set targets, to benchmark on our competitors we must **measure**. But we must go beyond the naive satisfaction of immediate customer wants. We need to look at our internal organisation structure and processes to identify improvements which will eventually lead to greater customer satisfaction and greater efficiency, or level of service. Thus, clearly, we need measurement to help us to identify whether improvements are worthwhile, to prioritise and monitor them, to benchmark our processes and set targets. Without measurement we have a quality improvement programme based on intuitive feel. This can still be worthwhile, but it is hard to maintain, it is hard to know that you are not slipping backwards and, above all, it is hard to know how far you've got to go. In reality there is little real choice: **we need measurement**. The problems are; what should we measure, how should we put measurement into place and how should we use measurement?

2.4 WHAT TO MEASURE

There are lots of dimensions to the question of what to measure, many of which are discussed in Chapter 6. Measurement should be **customer focused**, lest we forget that what we are trying to achieve is excellence in customer satisfaction. Measurement should also be **current and not historic**, so that information is available today to make decisions before we face serious problems. It should also be primarily obtained from our **internal business processes**, rather than from measuring outputs – outputs are too late, they correspond to dissatisfied customers. Perhaps, most of all, measurement must be **relevant**; our organisations are drowning in data, tied up in large databases not immediately of interest to issues at hand. The principle of collecting detailed data as you need it, to help in the formulation and solution of problems, as well as improvement rather than just prevention, was the major breakthrough achieved by the Japanese at shopfloor level compared to western corporate approaches.

Measurement must be **agreed**; there must be a clear consensus on the measurements relevant to monitoring our organisational performance. The debate about establishing such measures is in itself an important aspect of a quality improvement programme; it provides the opportunity to clarify and align improvements we are trying to achieve, it helps us all to work in the same direction, it helps us to analyse the deficiencies in our current performance. Early in a quality improvement programme, a simple unified framework for measurement can be obtained by considering the Cost of Quality (Chapter 4). Looking at where the organisation is wasting more money helps us to prioritise where action is needed, and helps us make decisions as to the cost effectiveness of prevention, and perhaps appraisal activities. A more fundamental unified approach is provided by the Critical Success Factors or Key Performance Indicators approach in Chapter 5. In each case, the alignment of improvement activities is facilitated by the agreement of the measurement system and the subsequent opportunities to review and refocus.

2.5 PUTTING MEASUREMENT INTO PLACE

There is an old Irish joke about the fact that if you want to get to where you are going you should not start from here. To make our quality improvement programme work, we are going to need measurement, but for most of us in our organisations measurement is a slightly uncomfortable word. If we have gone through the periods of naive productivity measurement, if we have overcomplicated analytical techniques driven only by experts, then there may be concern in the back of our heads that measurement may have more to do with staff evaluation than quality improvement. To put measurement into place, the crucial thing is that we must have a clear consensus as to why it is necessary and how we are going to do it. Top management must be clearly and visibly behind it, and they must take the trouble to explain to the organisation what it is, why it is being implemented and how.

Where do you start? The teaching of measurement tools to teams is one approach, aping the development of the original Quality Circles. For teams properly to utilise measurement techniques, some approach to problem- and improvement-formulation and resolution is needed. Familiarity with measurement techniques can be introduced to teams, but this alone cannot drive overall quality improvement on agreed central targets. Fundamentally, the measurement process is an essential part of the management of a quality improvement programme and must be driven from the Steering Group through the normal management channels. An ultimate approach to this is presented in Chapter 5.

Measurement should be introduced slowly and carefully, with the correct educational provision for all staff and employees as it is introduced. The measurement system should be continuously reviewed and self-monitored. You must not make the mistake again of becoming bogged down in a bureaucratic measurement system that exists only for its own sake.

2.6 THE USE OF MEASUREMENT

Measurement should be used for immediate feedback to all staff involved in the improvement process. It should be used for decision making, should be visual and transparent and not complicated or obscure. Simple graphical presentations, equally understood by top management and the workforce, in a single standardised approach utilised throughout the organisation, has enormous benefit. There should be a deliberate policy to discourage or prevent diversity of presentation. A minimal set of tools for measurement and presentation should be established and used exclusively. Targets and direction of 'goodness' should always be shown on graphs.

For measurement to be of real value, it must be used not just as a communication medium or to provide encouragement, but for reaction from management when measurements start to go in the wrong direction, and to prioritise the distribution of resources. Measures should be continuously reviewed at board meetings and Steering Group meetings and appropriate action taken. There is no point to measurement without the systems to use it correctly.

3. A History of Measuring Quality

3.1 INTRODUCTION

The establishment and adoption of measures and standards indicates a conscious effort to achieve conformity, to reduce variation, to control a certain quality feature, perhaps with the aim of replicating a desirable outcome or to make improvements on current performance. Measures and standards were also developed to compare one product with another and to ascertain 'value for money'. Also, by measuring and gaining understanding of the past, it may be possible to make predictions about the future.

In this chapter, we examine some of the individuals and concepts that are significant in the history of quality measurement. We try to relate them to a certain time and place in history. The period covered is from about 2000 BC to the present day, not in equal measure but in reflection of the importance of the different eras.

3.2 FROM ANTIQUITY TO THE FIRST WORLD WAR

The early Egyptians devised measures of length (the cubit) and also area (squared cubit). The 'royal cubit' was accepted and used as the master standard for linear measurements. They were also able to calculate the area of a circle and used a more accurate value for pi than any of the other ancient civilisations. They were the first to establish the 365¼-day year and divide it into 12 months with 24 hours per day. Using these measures and their flair for arithmetic and geometry they were able to develop basic geographical maps and star charts and also to predict the timing and extent of the periodic Nile flooding.

The earliest evidence of the strict control of quality, though, is often cited as the Code of Law of Hammurabi, King of Babylon, circa 1800 BC. The uniformity of the Babylonian weights and measures is well established as also is the quality of the Babylonian weapons of war.

The ancient Greeks have also left us many reminders of the quality of design, architecture and art that their civilisations were able to produce. In the fields of philosophy, science and mathematics, Pythagoras, Plato and Archimedes rapidly spring to mind.

Later, the Romans continued these traditions and are perhaps particularly remembered for their engineering skills and their ability to construct bridges, aqueducts, roads and buildings to standardised designs.

Nearer to home

Standards of weights were first introduced into England during the early part of the Middle Ages, in Saxon times. It was some three centuries later that statutes defining length and area were formulated, during the reign of Edward I (1239-1307).

It was also during the Middle Ages that the various trades' and craftsmen's guilds were established by master craftsmen, both in England and throughout the rest of Europe. These associations set standards for quality, working conditions and wages in an effort to protect and enhance the livelihoods of their members; the Guild Act in England stated that the wardens of the crafts were appointed 'to see the work to be good and right'. The same period saw the rise of the merchant classes and a move towards living in towns.

Manufacturing, however, was still carried out mainly by individuals or perhaps small groups of people. Quality could be said to be operator-controlled; the person supplying the goods or services dealt directly with the end user, establishing his needs and receiving feedback on satisfaction – a type of bespoke operation.

The Industrial Revolution, which began in Britain sometime after the middle of the eighteenth century, was to make a radical change in this respect. Based on ample deposits of iron and coal, and starting mainly in the textile industry – following inventions by people such as Hargreaves, Arkwright and Compton – mechanisation meant that manufacturing began to be increasingly centred in large factories. People moved from the land to work in the new industrial regions located around mining areas – Manchester, Newcastle, Glasgow and Birmingham.

In many areas of manufacturing, the skills of the craftsman were no longer needed and poorly-educated workers were recruited to operate the machines that satisfied the demand for exports. The owners of the business frequently delegated the running of the factory to managers, and the workforce became mere machine operators.

Adam Smith (1723–90), a professor at Glasgow University, wrote that:

> *The directors of such companies, being the managers rather of other people's money than of their own, it cannot well be expected that they should watch over it with the same anxious vigilance with which the partners in a private co-partnery frequently watch over their own . . . Negligence and profusion . . . must always prevail more or less, in the management of the affairs of such a company . . . The only trades which it seems possible for a joint stock company to carry on successfully . . . are those of which all the operations are capable of being reduced to what is called a routine, or such a uniformity of method as admits of little or no variation.*

It is a logical consequence of the Industrial Revolution that manufacturing should become increasingly concerned with uniformity, variance reduction and control. This is the origin of the need for measurement in modern manufacturing.

A friend of Smith, the inventor James Watt (1769–1848), and his colleague Matthew Boulton (1770–1842), obviously agreed with this point of view at their Soho Foundry where they manufactured the famous steam engines. They drew up detailed specifications, controlled materials and components, developed standard operating procedures and planned production flows. Records were kept on all aspects of the process and the profit accruing from the sale of each machine was calculated.

The situation in America

Although Britain was the birthplace of the Industrial Revolution and for a time was the world's wealthiest nation, the rest of Europe and the United States of America were not far behind. In America, Eli Whitney (1765–1825), the inventor of the cotton gin (for mechanically extracting cotton fibre from its seed pods), applied mass production techniques to the manufacture of 10,000 muskets for the US army. He speeded up the assembly operation by creating jigs – templates or moulds – that ensured that the manufactured parts were identical and therefore interchangeable.

During this period, responsibility for quality control was in the hands of the supervisors and Whitney analysed work loads to determine how many operators a supervisor could manage effectively.

Another American, Frederick Winslow Taylor (1856–1917), developed work analysis much further and created what he called Scientific Management – also known as Taylorism. Stop watches were given to foremen (whose duties were now redefined), jobs were broken down into their component elements, and times to achieve an optimum performance were recorded and became work standards. Technical standards were also created, by engineers and other specialists. Differential piece rates were introduced. In *Principles of Scientific Management* (1911) Taylor explained that 'What we hoped to ultimately determine was . . . how many foot-pounds of work a man could do in a day'.

Taylor's objective seems to have been to de-humanise the workforce and create a group of robots who blindly followed the laid-down instructions. Although many of the principles advocated by Taylor were taken up by several companies in the US, in Britain there was much resistance from the stronger labour movements resulting in the impact here being much weaker. Interestingly, Taylor's works were translated into Japanese.

One of the consequences of Taylorism was that supervisors now had more people reporting to them. They also had extra duties brought about by the increasing complexity and size of many manufacturing organisations as the use of mass production methods spread. In order that supervisors could concentrate more on production issues, by the end of the nineteenth century it was common for the quality to be checked by inspectors who had no direct involvement with, or responsibility for, the production process. Inspection as an approach to monitoring quality became a separate function.

3.3 THE DEVELOPMENT OF STATISTICAL QUALITY CONTROL

The advent of the First World War stimulated the need for more mass production and more inspection. The Technical Inspection Association was formed in Britain soon after the war and was incorporated as the Institute of Engineering Inspection in 1922. (This became the Institute of Quality Assurance in 1972).

However, 100 per cent inspection as a method of assuring quality to customers is not 100 per cent reliable, even if the inspection criteria are clearly defined and understood. It is also very time consuming and expensive and adds another link in the chain between manufacturer and customer.

In America in the 1920s, the telecommunications giant, Western Electric, was looking for a more rigorous quality control method, to increase customer confidence in, and support for, their instruments and appliances. In 1924 they set up the Inspection Engineering Department at their Bell Laboratories in New York and it was there, in the same year, that Dr Walter A. Shewhart and his co-workers designed the first control charts and started work on other techniques which applied statistical methods to the measurement and control of quality. Shewhart is generally regarded as the inventor of the control chart and the founder of what is now known as Statistical Process Control, or SPC for short.

One important feature of Shewhart's control chart is that it again necessitates quality measurement and quality control being applied at the point of manufacture rather than purely at the end of the line. With SPC, instead of inspecting work at the end of the line, critical steps in a process are sampled regularly and the measurements taken are recorded chronologically on control charts.

Various chart interpretation rules that have been developed allow the process operator to estimate whether the process is still in (statistical) control or not, i.e. whether the process is likely to be producing conforming outputs or not. If the latter is the case, then the process can be stopped and the cause of the out–of–control condition can be investigated and remedied before resuming production. Excessive incidence of non–conforming product is prevented during the process instead of being appraised at the end of the process. The opportunities for reducing nonconformities and for making cost savings, when compared with end–of–the–line inspection, are obvious.

The methodology can also bring about further quality improvements. Shewhart stressed the difference between 'common' causes of variation and 'special' or 'assignable' causes. The former are part of the system and beyond the operator's control; the latter can be assigned to a specific circumstance. The initial work of setting up the control charts necessitates the removal of as many of the special causes as possible so that the process runs in statistical control, demonstrating only common causes of variation. Similarly, during use, additional special causes may present themselves for removal and also management can take steps to remove some of the common causes and thus improve the overall variability of the process.

In 1925, one of Shewhart's colleagues, Harold E. Dodge, developed statistically–based methods of acceptance sampling: methods which allow the user to get an accurate appreciation of the quality of a consignment by inspecting and measuring only a part of it.

Investigations into the use of statistical methods to analyse variation had been carried out on both sides of the Atlantic since the end of the nineteenth century and it was in Britain, also in 1925, that R.A. Fisher (later Sir Ronald) published a work detailing initial experiments at Rothamstead Agricultural Research Station concerning potato yields.

Shewhart's *Economic Control of Quality of Manufactured Product* was published in America in 1931 and it was following his invited lectures at the University of London in 1932 that the Industrial and Agricultural Section of the Royal Statistical Society was formed. 1935 saw the publication of Fisher's *The Design of Experiments* and also the first British Standard on quality control. Developed by E.S. Pearson, BS 6000 was entitled *Application of Statistical Methods to Industrial Standardisation and Quality Control*.

The Second World War led to the rapid deployment of statistical techniques for measuring, evaluating and controlling quality – both in the UK and in the USA. Indirectly, it also paved the way for the revolution in the emphasis on quality management as the driving force for manufacturing excellence that has made Japan the world power that it is today.

In some industries, the last 50 years have seen the level of product defects being no longer routinely measured in percentages (parts per hundred), but in parts per million and even parts per billion. Again, in some areas, product quality is simply taken for granted; the market differentiator is seen as quality of service and therefore customer satisfaction levels become the key area to measure. As the world shrinks, business survival depends on quality. According to Armand Feigenbaum, quality is now the single most important force in organisational success and growth and, as such, the need for the measurement of internal and external performance has become crucial.

In the remainder of this chapter, we examine the messages of some of the quality experts, or gurus, who have, since the Second World War, contributed to quality achievement and measurement.

3.4 Dr W. Edwards Deming

Edwards Deming was born in Iowa in 1900 and was awarded his PhD in Mathematical Physics from Yale in 1928. He joined the United States Department of Agriculture, and in 1936 he came to England to study for a time under Fisher.

Deming had met Shewhart in 1927 and worked closely with him thereafter. Whereas Shewhart had concentrated on manufacturing processes, Deming believed that the same concepts could be applied in other areas. In 1939, when Deming moved to the National Bureau of the Census he applied Shewhart's statistical techniques to routine clerical operations. This resulted in some processes showing a six-fold productivity improvement, massive savings and the census report being published earlier than usual.

Attempts to meet the increased demand for materials for the war effort in America meant that many unskilled personnel were recruited by the manufacturing industries. Quality levels fell as a result and, in 1942, courses to teach various statistical approaches for the measurement and control of quality were quickly organised throughout the USA, some 31,000 personnel undergoing training. Both Deming and Shewhart were active in this effort and Deming himself led 23 courses. His training in his own and Shewhart's methods, of designers, inspectors and engineers, resulted in substantial reductions in scrap and rework together with productivity improvements. (Several people involved with this training programme banded together in 1946 to establish the American Society for Quality Control).

The gains in the use of statistical techniques for quality control made during the war were short-lived, both here and in the USA. In the boom market that developed, everything would sell, regardless of quality. Furthermore, many of the managers running the factories were not fully committed to the approach. To quote Deming from Nancy R. Mann's *The Keys to Excellence*, published in 1985:

The courses were well-received by engineers, but management paid no attention to them. Management did not understand that they had to get behind improvement of quality and carry out their obligations from the top down. Any instabilities can help to point out specific times or locations of local problems. Once these local problems are removed, there is a process that will continue until someone changes it. Changing the process is management's responsibility. And we failed to teach them that.

Shortly after the war, Deming went twice to Japan to assist Japanese statisticians in studies of housing and nutrition, and for preparation of the census of 1951. It was during these visits that he met members of JUSE, the Union of Japanese Scientists and Engineers, which had been founded in 1946 to aid the rebuilding of Japan. A delegation from Bell Telephone Laboratories also visited Japan at about this time to demonstrate how the statistical methods, as developed and taught by Shewhart and Deming, could be used for controlling and improving quality in the Japanese telecommunications industry. Deming was invited to Japan again, this time by JUSE.

The Japanese were aware of BS 6000 and also the Z–1 American Standards developed during the war but, because the statistical approach was difficult to understand, it was not accepted widely. Ishikawa, in *What is Total Quality Control? The Japanese Way*, wrote

In management, Japan also lagged behind, using the so-called Taylor method in certain quarters . . . Quality control was totally dependent on inspection, and not every product was sufficiently inspected. In those days Japan was still competing with cost and price but not with quality. It was literally still the age of 'cheap and poor' products.

Deming returned to Japan in June 1950 and taught over 500 managers and engineers about the importance of understanding and controlling variation and the use of control charts, in a series of eight–day courses. He also introduced a systematic approach to problem solving and improvement, known variously as the Shewhart cycle (by Deming himself), the Deming cycle and the PDCA cycle.

This Plan, Do, Check, Action cycle, shown in Figure 3.1, is an improvement methodology involving a feedback loop. The normal tendency, without the discipline imposed by the cycle, is to skimp on

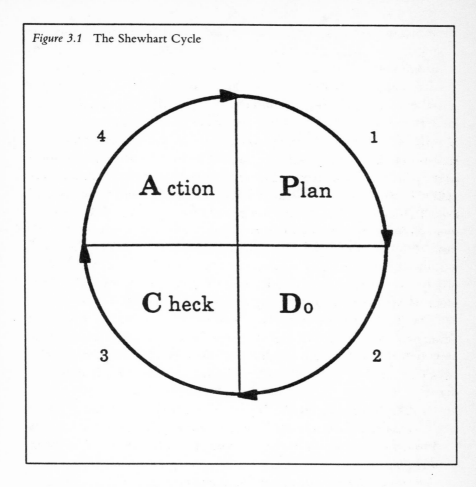

Figure 3.1 The Shewhart Cycle

the planning and checking phases (target setting and monitoring), and perhaps to concentrate on the doing element. This leads to reacting or fire-fighting instead of a controlled assessment of the situation and then further action based on fact. It has been suggested that this may be because of the results-oriented society we live in, where doing is seen as being productive (and is easily measurable) and planning may be seen as procrastination.

Deming was determined to avoid a repetition of the situation that he had seen develop in America after the war. He made arrangements through JUSE to address senior managers to make them aware of the roles and responsibilities that they must take on board if Japanese industry was to turn itself around by making improvements in its quality performance so that they could compete internationally. He stressed the need for working closely with suppliers to improve the uniformity and reliability of incoming materials and also the need for maintenance of equipment.

He also emphasised the importance of the consumer and, in subsequent visits in 1951 and 1952, when he addressed many more engineers and top managers, he supplemented his usual courses with lessons on consumer research and modern methods of sampling. He taught that '. . . the consumer is the most important part of the production line', and his courses committed his students to carrying out door-to-door surveys in order to measure consumer requirements.

In the West, it was not until the 1970s that Deming started to make an impact. In 1980 when NBC, the American broadcasting company, made a documentary entitled *If Japan Can, Why Can't We?*, many more became aware of his concepts. However, Deming is constantly reviewing and refining his ideas and his more recent work is more management-based than statistically-based. His famous 14 Points for Management were produced to help people understand and implement '. . . the total transformation of Western style of management' that he believes to be necessary. The 14 points, and more of Deming's recent thinking are captured in his 1986 book, *Out of the Crisis*.

Deming was awarded the Shewhart Medal by the American Society for Quality Control in 1956 and, in 1960, he became the first to be awarded the Second Order of the Sacred Treasure, the highest decoration that can be conferred on a non-Japanese. He was awarded the National Medal of Technology in America in 1987.

3.5 DR JOSEPH M. JURAN

Another recipient of the Second Order of the Sacred Treasure, though not until 1980, is Joseph Juran. Juran was born in Rumania in 1904 and moved to America at an early age. He trained as an engineer but his career has been varied; industrial executive, government administrator, university professor, labour arbitrator, corporate director and management consultant. He went to Japan in 1954, also at the invitation of JUSE.

With his broad experience in management, coupled with his expertise in quality methods, he was able to discuss the wider issues of quality measurement and to appeal to senior Japanese managers. His lectures focused on planning and organisational issues, management's responsibility for quality, and the need to set goals and targets for improvement. He emphasised that quality control should be conducted as an integral part of management control. His lectures were followed up at more junior management levels by JUSE and the Japanese Standards Association. Large companies started internal training, courses for foremen were offered on national radio and booklets were made available at newspaper kiosks.

In the first edition of the *Quality Control Handbook*, published in 1951 and edited (and mainly written) by Juran, he coined the phrase 'There is gold in the mine'. This was a reference to the huge cost saving that can be made by measuring and resolving quality problems. However, it is not at the surface; you have to dig for it. Juran knew that making quality improvements is not easy; there are many barriers and obstacles to be overcome. Juran has used the measurement of costs attributable to quality problems within an organisation to capture the attention of senior management in the West.

Quality costs can also be used to prioritise and monitor improvement activity. Juran believes that at least 80 per cent of quality problems result from the systems and procedures laid down by management and therefore exhortations to the workforce to try harder will only serve to alienate them. Instead, he advocates the use of cross-functional management teams for achieving quality improvement. He teaches a project–by–project approach to solving quality problems and was probably the first to recommend the use of the Pareto principle for prioritising actions; identifying and tackling the 'vital few' problems and not the 'useful many'.

Juran also stresses the need for planning for quality. He sees quality planning as part of the quality trilogy of quality planning, quality control and quality improvement.

Quality control is the responsibility of the operating personnel, maintaining the status quo by following procedures, monitoring outputs and fire-fighting if necessary. Quality improvement has already been discussed and it concerns the measurement and reduction of what Juran calls chronic quality problems.

Quality planning uses the lessons learned whilst making improvements to ensure that similar problems are avoided in the future. In *Juran on Planning for Quality*, published in 1988, the key elements in implementing company-wide strategic quality planning are seen as identifying customers and their needs; establishing optimal quality goals; creating measurements of quality; planning processes capable of meeting quality goals under operating conditions and producing continuing results in improved market share, premium prices, and a reduction of error rates in the office and factory.

Each stage of the planning process has inputs and outputs. Throughout the process there are a series of suppliers (of the inputs) and customers (for the outputs). Juran sees these supplier-customer relationships extending beyond the planning phase and on through all the steps involved in actually supplying the goods or service to the end user or consumer. The public in general may be regarded as a customer if the product or service (or the provision of it) impacts sufficiently on it.

Measurement must be introduced throughout this supplier-customer chain to evaluate, control and improve what the customer (internal or external) receives. The type, frequency and method of measurement will depend on the stage of the process and the people who will use it.

Juran, like Deming, has been critical of senior management in the West but he sees the 1990s as the time when the improvement efforts made by western organisations over the last decade will finally bear fruit.

3.6 Dr Armand V. Feigenbaum

Armand Feigenbaum was the third major American quality expert to visit Japan in the 1950s. Now 72, he is somewhat younger than the two previous gurus. In the 1950s, as Head of Quality at the General Electric Company, he had extensive contacts with Japanese companies such as Toshiba and Hitachi and his 1951 book was translated into Japanese.

Feigenbaum argued for the involvement of all functions within the quality process, not just the manufacturing area. The idea is to build quality in at an early stage instead of relying on process control and inspection further down the line. His concept of Total Quality Control extends the administrative function to include the measurement and control of quality at every stage, from customer specification and sales, through design, engineering, assembly and shipment. In *Total Quality Control*, published in 1983, Total Quality Control is seen as providing the structure and tools for managing quality so that there is a continuous emphasis throughout the organisation on quality leadership. The need for quality–mindedness throughout all levels is emphasised and quality control within the organisation is seen as both:

- a channel for communication for product quality information and
- a means of participation in the overall plant quality programme

A Total Quality System is defined by him as:

The agreed company-wide and plant-wide operating work structure, documented in effective, integrated technical and managerial procedures, for guiding the co-ordinated actions of the people, the machines, and the information of the company and plant in the best and most practical ways to assure customer quality satisfaction and economical costs of quality.

Operating quality costs can be divided into:

- Prevention costs – including quality planning
- Appraisal costs – including inspection
- Internal failure costs – including scrap and rework
- External failure costs – including warranty costs, product recall

Reductions in operating quality costs result from establishing a total quality system for two reasons:

- Lack of existing effective customer–oriented standards may mean that current product quality is not optimal, given use
- Expenditure on prevention can lead to a severalfold reduction in internal and external failure costs.

Dr Feigenbaum founded the International Academy for Quality and is a past president of the American Society for Quality Control, which presented him with the Edwards Medal and the Lancaster Award for his international contributions to quality and productivity. In 1988, he was appointed to the board which oversees the Malcolm Baldrige National Quality Award Programme and, in 1991, the 40th Anniversary edition of *Total Quality Control* was published.

3.7 DR KAORU ISHIKAWA

Dr Ishikawa was born in 1915 and graduated from Tokyo University in 1939 with a degree in applied chemistry. His name will perhaps be best known to many people from the Ishikawa Diagram, otherwise known as the Cause & Effect or Fishbone Diagram. Ishikawa invented the diagram (in 1952) to supplement the other tools and techniques that he advocated for the measurement, control and improvement of processes in (mainly) Japanese companies for many years until his death in 1989.

After the war, he returned to Tokyo University and in 1948 began to study statistical methods. By 1949, he had joined JUSE's

Quality Control Research Group and, following Deming's visit in 1950, began teaching the application of statistical methods for quality control, making it compulsory for his engineering students at the university.

Ishikawa's contribution to the turn-round of Japan's industry since the war can hardly be overstated. As well as teaching the techniques of quality control directly to all levels within diverse organisations, he pioneered the Quality Circle movement in Japan, initiated quality conferences, contributed regularly to quality journals and worked closely with the Japanese Industrial Standards Committee which led to him becoming chairman of the Japanese Chapter of the International Standards Organisation in 1977.

Ishikawa had the rare ability to adopt technical methods and make them accessible and palatable to all levels within an organisation. In particular, he championed the use of what are commonly called the Seven Tools of Quality Control:

- Pareto charts – to prioritise action
- Cause & Effect diagrams – to identify causes of variation
- Stratification – to divide data into subsets
- Check sheets – for data collection
- Histograms – to display variation graphically
- Scatter diagrams – to confirm relationships between two factors
- Shewhart's control charts and graphs – to monitor and control variation.

The same set of tools was used on a team basis at all levels and by all functions within organisations for the measurement, evaluation, control and improvement of all business activities, not just for quality control of the product. Furthermore, because the output from the use of the tools is graphical, the information displayed can be understood by all, helping to reduce misunderstandings and obviate communication problems.

Ishikawa's book *Guide to Quality Control*, based on articles written for the *Quality Control for the Foreman* journal, is a classic text describing the use of these tools. One of Ishikawa's pet themes, highlighted in the book, is the accurate collection and use of data; he argued that all data should be treated with suspicion and historical databases should be ignored. Data should be collected as and where it is needed.

Company-wide quality

Ishikawa was a key player in the Company-wide Quality Control movement which started in Japan around 1955, following the visits of Deming and Juran. Company-wide quality control necessitates measurement by all. Everyone studies statistical methods. Every function and all levels participate in the improvement process; research, design, engineering, manufacturing, sales, clerical, personnel, etc. Quality control concepts and methods are used to measure, monitor and improve incoming raw materials, manufacturing processes, personnel issues and sales problems. In Ishikawa's concept, quality does not mean only the quality of the product but also after-sales service, quality of management, the company itself and the human being. As a result:

- Product quality improves and becomes uniform. Defects are reduced.
- Product reliability is improved.
- Cost is reduced.
- Productivity increases and it becomes possible to make rational production schedules.
- Wasteful work and rework are reduced.
- Technique is established and improved.
- Expenses for inspection and testing are reduced.
- Contracts between vendor and vendee are rationalised.
- The sales market is enlarged.
- Better relationships are established between departments.
- False data and reports are reduced.
- Discussions are carried out more freely and democratically.
- Meetings are operated more smoothly.
- Repairs and installations of equipment and facilities are done more rationally.
- Human relations are improved.

Quality Control circles

Quality control (QC) circles are a major feature of company-wide quality control and illustrate Ishikawa's commitment to education and measurement for all. In 1962 Ishikawa became chairman of the editorial board of a low-price journal entitled *Quality Control for the Foreman*. This was published by JUSE and built on the success of another regular JUSE publication, *Statistical Quality Control*, which originated in 1950. The purpose of the new magazine was to get the message and techniques of quality measurement to the operators in the front line. QC circles began in Japan as study groups – workers and their foremen being encouraged to read and discuss the concepts and methods advocated in *Quality Control for the Foreman* and then to try the approaches in their own work areas.

The nature and role of circles varies between companies but the following is a general guide: Small groups from 5 to 10 people from the same work area meet voluntarily on a regular basis to discuss, investigate, measure and analyse work-related problems. The circle is led by a foreman or one of the workers and the seven tools of quality control are used. Depending on the organisation, solutions to problems identified by the circle are either presented to management for authorisation before implementation, or the team has authority to implement directly. Circle members receive no direct financial reward for their improvements.

The aims of the QC circle activities are to:

- Contribute to the improvement and development of the enterprise;
- Respect human relations and build a happy workshop offering job satisfaction;
- Deploy human capabilities fully and draw out infinite potential.

The QC circle concept spread rapidly, both within manufacturing companies and also into service organisations. Encouraged by books, seminars, lectures, annual conferences and visits to other organisations, the number of individuals involved in circles activity in Japan is now in excess of ten million. Ishikawa was central to masterminding much of this growth and in laying down the ground rules for circle activities.

Ishikawa is often regarded as the 'father of Japanese quality'. He was awarded the Deming Prize, the Nihon Keizai Press Prize, the Industrial Standardisation Prize and the Grant Award. The latter was presented by the American Society for Quality Control in 1971 in recognition of his education programme on quality control.

3.8 DR GENICHI TAGUCHI AND DR SHIGEO SHINGO

Taguchi and Shingo are two further Japanese quality gurus whose ideas contributed tremendously to Japan's post-war turn-round. Both evolved methods for the prevention of quality problems in manufacture and for the design of efficient processes – but used very different approaches. Their methods are now finding increasing use in the West.

TAGUCHI

Genichi Taguchi was born in Japan in 1924. When the Nippon Telephone and Telegraph Company established its Electrical Communications Laboratory (ECL) in 1949, he was recruited to improve the efficiency of their research and development activities. His first book was published in 1951 and earned him the Deming award for literature on quality. The book introduced statistical methods for minimising the number of trials or tests that need to be carried out in order to arrive at a satisfactory design. In 1954–5, Taguchi visited the Indian Statistical Institute where he conducted several experiments and also met Shewhart and Fisher. Part of Taguchi's methodology is based on the work begun by Fisher in England in the 1920s, but expanded and adapted for industrial applications.

During the 12 years that Taguchi spent with ECL, he consulted widely amongst many Japanese companies, including Toyota. Like

Ishikawa, he has been able to simplify complex statistical methods and make them comprehensible to non-academics. Taguchi's methods, which in essence build quality into processes and products at the design stage, were therefore available to many Japanese companies from the 1950s. The diagram shown in Figure 3.2 illustrates the relative contributions of the different approaches to quality control used in Japan since World War II.

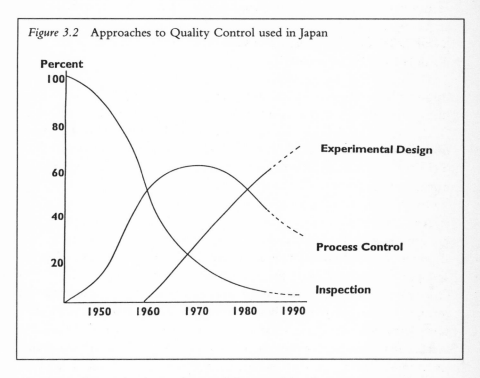

Figure 3.2 Approaches to Quality Control used in Japan

Taguchi methods can be used for trouble-shooting in production but their main application is in the design of new production processes and, increasingly, new products. Within a process, the number of factors that contribute to the quality and consistency of the output can be many. Which are the important ones, and how important are they? Are they always important or only under certain conditions? To test out and measure the effect of all of the possible combinations of variables and at different levels would be an impossible task. How long can you wait to get a new product to market?

Conventionally, the need to get new products to market quickly can mean that processes are set up based on previous experience, a few trials that nearly worked, and with fingers crossed as production starts, in the hope of meeting the agreed deadline. As problems occur, they are dealt with as far as possible by problem-solving and at great cost in terms of defective items produced, time wasted, customer dissatisfaction, etc. The process variables are subsequently 'twiddled' in an effort to improve consistency of output and minimise the production of defectives.

Instead, Taguchi's approach uses a standard set of tables to optimise the number of experimental trials that need to be carried out initially. These 'orthogonal arrays' reduce the number of tests dramatically by giving an experimental design pattern which does not measure the effect of every possible combination or level of factors but gives sufficient measure on each for decisions to be made. Further trials to home in more precisely on the optimum levels can be made if required. As an example of the power of the method: seven different factors each at two levels would require 128 experiments if tackled conventionally; Taguchi uses just eight. For six factors at five levels, equivalent to 15,625 combinations, Taguchi would carry out 25 experiments initially.

By carrying out the design experiments, the optimum level and relative importance of each variable is established with regard to the sensitivity of the process to environmental and other uncontrollable factors. Efficient and robust processes can then be set up using this data, and SPC can be used to monitor and control quality characteristics in the critical areas identified.

The 'Quality Loss Function', developed by Taguchi in the early 1970s, may be used to measure and evaluate design decisions on a financial basis. The cost element is defined as 'loss imparted by the product to society from the time the product is shipped'. The loss includes not only the normal company costs of scrap, rework, downtime, warranty, etc, but also costs to the customer in terms of poor product performance and reliability, which themselves may result in the manufacturer losing future business. To minimise this loss to society, the variation from the target, for any particular quality characteristic, must also be minimised – usually at extra cost. By using the quality loss function – a mathematical formula – decisions can be made to determine whether additional costs in production will actually prove to be worthwhile in the market place. For this reason, the loss function is generally used at the last phase of designing a new product or process, after the design has already been optimised as fully as possible.

Since 1980, more and more American companies have implemented Taguchi methodology – including Xerox, Ford and ITT. In Europe, with one or two exceptions such as Lucas, Taguchi's approach found little application until, in 1987, the Institute of Statisticians organised a conference in London to publicise the methods. The UK Taguchi Club (now part of the Quality Methods Association) was formed later that year.

SHINGO

Born in Japan in 1909, Shigeo Shingo is perhaps not as well known in the West as the two previous quality gurus although the impact of his work, especially in Japan, has been immense. After graduating in Mechanical Engineering at Yamanashi Technical College in 1930, he joined the Taipei Railway Factory in Taiwan where he introduced the methods of scientific management. In 1945 he became a professional consultant with the Japan Management Association where, as Education Department Chairman in 1951, he first became aware of statistical quality control techniques.

From 1955 he was responsible for industrial engineering and factory improvement training at Toyota Motor Company. In the period between 1956 and 1958, whilst working at Mitsubishi Heavy Industries in Nagasaki, Shingo was responsible for halving the time for the hull assembly of a 65,000 ton supertanker from four months to two months. His methods quickly spread to other Japanese shipyards. In 1959 he left the Japan Management Association and established the Institute of Management Improvement.

From 1961 Shingo started to develop *poka-yoke* systems. *Poka-yoke* literally means mistake-proofing and was the name he adopted for the technique after he received complaints for calling the method fool-proofing (*baka-yoke*). Most people will be aware of the basic idea. In the West, we often see this approach where safety is an issue but in Japan it is also used extensively where quality is the main concern. Interestingly, *poka-yoke* systems, by using devices which prevent defects from occurring, obviate the need for measurement. *Poka-yoke* systems in general involve two phases: the detection aspect and the regulatory aspect. Detection can be accomplished by various means: physical contact, limit switches, photo-electric cells, pressure-sensitive switches, thermostats, etc. Regulation can be by either giving a warning (e.g. flashing light, alarm buzzer) or by taking control (prevention, automatically shutting a machine down) – or both.

Shingo distinguished between 'errors' and 'defects', the latter being caused by the former. He recognised that people do make mistakes, for a variety of reasons, but the errors need not result in defects. His method is to stop the process whenever an error occurs and to establish the source of the error by inspection, and then to prevent its recurrence. *Poka-yoke* devices, in effect, give 100 per cent inspection, but during the process when prevention is possible and not after the event when it is too late. Using Shingo's concept of Zero Quality Control, zero defects can be achieved.

Shingo had been a firm believer in the application of statistical process control since he first learned about it. Gradually, as he did more and more work with *poka-yoke* systems, his enthusiasm for SPC waned. Improvement from statistical methods comes from the detection and measurement of defects and a reaction to them; his methods prevent defects. Furthermore, statistical methods use sampling techniques; his *poka-yoke* methods allow for 100 per cent inspection and make measurement unnecessary.

By 1977, he was finally released from the spell of statistical methods when a plant in Matsushita's Washing Machine Division had seven months of defect-free operation in their drain-pipe assembly line involving 23 workers producing 30,000 units per month. Since then, many more companies have run for several months without producing defects by using Shingo's Zero Quality Control methods.

Poka-yoke systems improve process efficiency, save waste and reduce costs: critical factors for measurement and improvement in any organisation. In 1969 whilst working for Toyota Shingo developed a system known as single-minute exchange of die, or SMED. This improvement methodology similarly reduces waste. The purpose of SMED is to minimise the amount of time taken when making changeovers. It reduces downtime and increases production flexibility, obviating the need for long production runs and large batches. Inventory can be reduced dramatically as there is less need to maintain stock to cover for the hold-ups.

At Toyota, the set-up time for a 1,000 ton press was four hours, twice as long as it took Volkswagen in West Germany. Within six months, Shingo had reduced Toyota's set-up time for the operation to one and a half hours. Following this initial success, a new target was given – three minutes! Shingo achieved this within a further three months! Other examples show set-up times being reduced from six hours to six minutes and work-in-progress inventory being slashed by 90 per cent.

Set-up time is made up of two elements which can be measured separately: internal set-up time, when the machine must be stopped, and external set-up time, when the machine need not be stopped. The optimisation process involved converting as much internal set-up time to external set-up time as possible – and then relentlessly improving both aspects. The improvements are made by a variety of simplification and de-skilling methods: jigs, clamps, quick-release fastenings, standardisation of fittings, etc.

When production hold-ups are reduced dramatically by the application of SMED techniques and when output can be virtually guaranteed by zero defect production, Just-In-Time (JIT) operating methods, Kanban and non-stock production become possible. Shingo was a key player in the introduction of these approaches within several companies and Toyota's production system in particular.

Shingo was awarded the Yellow Ribbon Decoration in 1970 for his services in improving production. He wrote more than 14 major books, several of which have now been translated into English and other European languages. Shigeo Shingo died in 1990.

3.9 DR CLAUS MØLLER

Claus Møller is a Danish business economist who was educated in Copenhagen. He founded his company, Time Manager International (TMI), in 1975. Human relations training and customer service programmes are key areas of TMI's activities. The 'Putting People First' programmes have been run with several airlines including Japan Airlines. From 1984, management training in the Soviet Union was carried out as a contribution to perestroika and the modernisation of the Soviet economy. Møller's 'Management for Everyone' programme was started in 1987 for 16,000 people within the EEC to increase job satisfaction and improve team identity. The work resulted in the reduction of bureaucracy and improvement of productivity.

Møller's book, *Personal Quality*, was published in 1988. He has developed a series of grids and tables which allow individuals to measure and monitor their personal quality performance. He sees personal quality as the basis for all other types of quality and believes that to improve departmental quality, product quality, service quality and company quality, it is necessary to improve personal quality. The people who make the goods or deliver the service must be inspired to do their best in order to improve service to the customer. He sees personal development of the individual as the key. This philosophy is not unlike the thinking of Ishikawa, discussed earlier in the chapter.

Two standards for personal quality can usefully be measured. The IP-level, or ideal performance level, reflects a person's desires, expectations and demands concerning his or her performance; the AP-level, or actual performance level, is what a person is currently achieving. IP-level is established during the earliest years of life and is relatively stable and fixed when adulthood is reached. AP-level is not static but varies from situation to situation and from one minute to the next. It can be raised or lowered by external influences such as praise, recognition, reprimands, success and failure, etc. It has much to do with self-esteem.

The difference between your IP-level and your AP-level is the difference between what you are capable of achieving and what you are actually achieving; it represents the potential for development or improvement. Møller believes that high self-esteem leads to improved quality and producing good quality improves self-esteem; one feeds off the other. The lesson is clear: by encouraging, supporting and giving the opportunity for self-development, then quality improvements will follow.

3.10 HISTORICAL PERSPECTIVE

In this chapter we have examined the history of quality and its measurement from the time of the Babylonians to the present day. From the 3,500 plus years that have been reviewed, it is possible to pick out those periods, individuals and key themes that highlight the changes in approach that have taken place.

Perhaps the first turning point was the Industrial Revolution and the increasing use made of mass production techniques; this can be regarded as the origin of the need for measurement in modern manufacturing. About a hundred years later, Taylor and scientific management helped to establish inspection as a separate function: measuring quality and sorting the good from the bad at the end of the production line.

Although the development of SPC by Shewhart is highly significant, it was not until Deming took the technique to Japan in 1950 that it was used widely within industry for the measurement and control of processes. SPC put quality measurement and control back into the hands of the process operators. Deming also introduced the simple PDCA improvement cycle.

Juran's visits corrected the exclusive emphasis on statistical techniques by defining management's role in the continuous improvement process; quality was something that had to be managed just like other areas of the business. He also advocated the measurement of quality costs for identifying improvement opportunities and prioritising improvement activity; 'There is gold in the mine'.

Feigenbaum continued the message by stressing the need for quality in all areas of the business – Total Quality Control – and the need for administrative procedures to provide a link in the improvement process.

Ishikawa was a key player in the Company-Wide Quality movement; measurement for all. All functions, all levels used the same basic set of tools to monitor, control and improve all aspects of the business, not just quality. Ishikawa championed the use of the seven tools of quality control and also the growth of quality control circles.

Taguchi developed efficient methods for measuring quality at the design stage. Quality is built into products and processes. Shingo made zero defects possible by detecting mistakes and preventing them from becoming defects.

Claus Møller developed ways to measure personal quality and sees it as the basis for all other types of quality.

From 1950 until the mid 1970s, the progress, the new approaches and the changes were largely taking place in Japan. Industries in the West were increasingly losing out to competition from the Far East – steel, cars, shipbuilding, electrical goods, etc. It was not until the early 1980s that western management began to take 'Quality' seriously as a key to being competitive.

Some impetus in the UK has come from the introduction of BS 5750. Based on Defence Standards, and originally published in 1979, BS 5750 was brought into line with the ISO 9000 series of Standards for quality systems in 1987. (The ISO series, themselves, had been based on the original 1979 BS 5750 Standard). Registration to ISO 9000/BS 5750 has now become mandatory for many suppliers, and there can be little doubt that the disciplines imposed by the Standards can be a very good *starting point* for many organisations attempting to take the path towards Total Quality Management (TQM). Monitoring of suppliers, processes, inspection and test equipment, and other areas of the quality management system are covered by the Standards but there can be a danger of the system becoming solely a paper-generating exercise if the greater goals, to be achieved by pursuing TQM, go unrecognised.

Juran talked about the Quality Crisis in western industry in the early 1980s. Quality awareness was raised but it seldom resulted in changed behaviour and improved performance. But, as the 1980s progressed, more and more western companies went beyond awareness to achievement. In the main, these have been the ones in areas most affected by competition from the East; electronics and automotive companies have had to improve to survive.

In 1989, Florida Power and Light (FPL) became the first non-Japanese company to win the Deming Prize. By learning from Japanese companies, they completely reorganised the way they thought about their business. They set a target of 'Customer Satisfaction' as an objective for the corporation. Previously, they, like many western companies, had been inward-looking with regard to company targets and goals; the role of the customer within the company's definition of the improvement targets has often been assumed – or ignored.

FPL selected six measures to gauge their performance as it would be perceived by its customers: reliability of service; numbers of complaints received; breakdowns in power transmissions, etc. Driven by these customer-focused critical success factors, and a strong determination to achieve them, FPL made improvements and won the award. More on the critical success factors approach and FPL can be found in Chapter 5.

3.11 The picture today

Deming's message to 'delight your customers' is seen by many as the way to be competitive in today's markets and 'quality as perceived by the customer' has become a key aim for many companies. However, saying it does not make it happen. Customer-focused measures must be in place throughout business processes to ensure that the goal is being achieved. Some 'customer–care' programmes may give the initial impression of delighting customers but many lack real substance and depth; they may provide the surface gloss but no real improvement in service to customers.

Two tools which can be used to aid this process are Quality Function Deployment (QFD) and benchmarking. QFD originated in Japan, and is a process which starts by mapping customer requirements to potential product or service features. The idea is to make sure that the Voice of the Customer is heard throughout the business. The technique will be dealt with in Chapter 8.

Benchmarking is another tool which is finding increased use. Here, to establish realistic improvement targets, a search is made to identify best practice, typically from other organisations, in the selected part of the business process. This is described in Chapter 7.

4. The Cost of Quality

4.1 INTRODUCTION

A study of the Cost of Quality can provide a unifying approach to driving Quality Improvement in an organisation, and offers a basis for identifying and prioritising projects in a language which can be understood by everyone – that of money. However, it must be realised that whilst opportunities for improvement can be highlighted by a Cost of Quality exercise, the savings may not always be 'real' money, that is, they are not necessarily directly transferable to the bottom line.

For too long, many organisations have believed that improvements in the quality of products and services were not possible, because the cost of effecting the necessary changes was perceived as being too high. Typically, cost of quality is seen as being related only, for example, to areas such as inspection, or the laboratory facilities. The cost of failure, that is, the cost of getting it wrong, has often been overlooked, or at best been implicit within complex accounting procedures. Such costs are frequently accepted as a normal part of life within the manufacturing or service environment, and are not challenged. Some of the typical areas which often go unrecognised are shown in the diagram in Figure 4.1

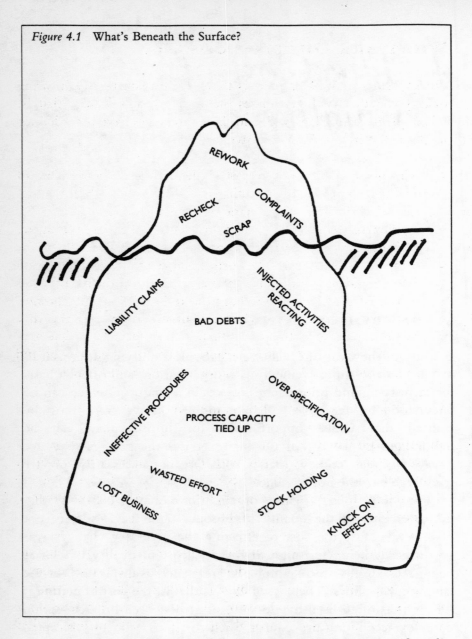

Figure 4.1 What's Beneath the Surface?

Very often performance of the organisation in terms of quality has been reported by means of, for example, scrap or rework data, and has not been translated into financial terms.

What are Quality Costs?

Quality costs may be defined as the cost of assuring and ensuring quality together with the losses incurred through failure, that is, when quality is not achieved, and these categories have been defined in BS6143, Part 2, 1990 as follows:

- **Appraisal cost.** The cost of evaluating the achievement of quality requirements including e.g. cost of verification and control performed at any stage of the quality loop.
- **Prevention cost.** The cost of any action taken to investigate, prevent or reduce the risk of nonconformity or defect.
- **Internal failure cost.** The costs arising within an organisation due to nonconformities or defects at any stage of the quality loop such as costs of scrap, rework, retest, re-inspection and redesign.
- **External failure cost.** The cost arising from delivery to a customer/user due to nonconformities or defects which may include the cost of claims against warranty, replacement and consequential losses and evaluation of penalties incurred.

We will now look at each of these in more detail.

A. Appraisal Costs

These are the costs associated with the measuring, evaluating or auditing of products, components or purchased materials to assure conformance with quality standards and performance requirements. Appraisal activities therefore might include:

- *Incoming material inspection* – costs incurred in determining the quality of vendor made products either by inspection on receipt, by inspection at source or by surveillance methods.
- *Inspection and Test* – the cost of checking the conformance of the product or service throughout its progress including final inspection.
- *Maintaining the accuracy of test equipment* – including the cost of operating the system that keeps the measuring instruments and

equipment in calibration.
- *Materials and services consumed* – the cost of materials, products and services consumed by destructive testing.
- *Evaluation of stocks* – includes the testing of stocks to evaluate degradation.

Typical appraisal cost categories might be:

- Incoming Inspection
- Work Process Audits
- Quality Measurement and Reporting
- In-house Appraisal
- Supplier Surveys
- Internal Audits
- Process Surveillance
- Stock Audit
- Laboratory Analysis
- Market Surveys
- Outside Contracted Appraisal Costs
- Sample Testing

– Receiving
– In process
– Final

B. Prevention Costs
These are the cost of actions to reduce or prevent non-conformance and might include:

- *The costs associated with personnel* engaged in planning, implementing and maintaining the quality system.
- *New product reviews* – the cost of evaluating designs and prototype samples (including testing wear trials), of writing specifications for raw materials, processes and products and other quality activities associated with new designs.
- *Training* – the cost of preparing training programmes for

attaining and improving quality performance and the cost of conducting them.

- *Process Control* – the costs incurred in identifying and controlling those process variables that affect quality.
- *Quality data acquisition and analysis* – this is the work of running the quality data system to acquire continuing information on quality performance. It includes analysis of this data to identify quality problems, to sound the alarms, initiate close examination, etc.
- *Quality reporting* – includes the work of summarising and publishing quality information.
- *Improvement projects* – includes the work of structuring and carrying out programmes for breakthrough to new levels of performance, that is, defect prevention programmes, awareness programmes.

Typical prevention cost categories might be:

- Customer Requirements Review
- Training Certification
- Packaging Qualification
- Failure Effects/Mode Analysis
- Review of Test Specifications
- Verification of Workmanship Standards
- Requirements Verification
- Work Process and Procedure
- Checking of Drawings
- Preventive Maintenance
- Process Capability Studies
- Process Instruction Review

C. Internal Failure Costs

These are the costs that would disappear if no defects existed in the product or service prior to delivery to the customer or in the service that supports the product. They may include:

- *Scrap, Seconds* – lost sales proceeds at first quality prices less the sales proceeds expected or achieved at reduced prices.
- *Rework, Reprocess, Repair* – the total additional costs incurred in manufacturing product over and above those that would have been incurred had the product been manufactured right first time.
- *Waste/Yield Losses* – the cost of material yields lower than might be attained by improved controls, including process yield.

Other costs may include:

- Work in Process – Overstocking of materials not immediately required
- Expenses – Expending more than needed for a required output
- Labour – Failure to achieve required output from standard minute values
- Downtime – the cost of idle facilities resulting from defective services, e.g. breakdown maintenance losses, poor material processing losses, planning errors.
- Writedowns – due to over-purchase of raw materials, failure to deliver goods on time, materials not to specification, etc.

D. External Failure Costs
Distinguished from internal failure costs by the fact that defects are found by the customer. They may include:

- *Complaints Adjustments/Allowances* – all costs of investigation and adjustment of complaints attributable to defective product or service.
- *Returned Material* – all costs associated with the receipt and replacement of defective product.

Typical failure cost categories might be:

- Bad Debts
- Premium Freight Costs

- Product Liability Costs
- Loss of Customer Goodwill
- Failure Analysis
- 100% Test to Sort
- Corrective Action
- Re-entry of Data
- Warranty Expense
- Scrap (includes obsolete material and inventory shortages)
- Rework
- Sales Travel and Time on Problems
- Engineering Travel and Time on Problems
- Redesign
- Change of Orders
- Excess Inventory Cost
- Costs of Late Product/Service

4.3 HOW TO INTRODUCE COST OF QUALITY

Collection

Once an understanding of the elements of cost of quality has been gained, and the potential areas for measuring cost of quality have been identified, the collection of the information can commence. However, experience has shown that prior to collection of the necessary data it is essential that all those who will be involved in its evaluation should be made aware of the purpose of the exercise. For example, it is possible that some managers will see this as just another cost cutting exercise, and construct defensive barriers with their heads well below the parapet! It must be explained that having obtained the information, the organisation will be seeking continuous improvement, and therefore it is important that all hidden costs of quality are 'put on the table' at this stage. In addition, the use of inappropriate comparisons must be avoided. Understanding of the need, and the process to be adopted will remove the element of fear which can so easily disrupt the whole programme. The aim is to reduce Quality Costs over time, as illustrated in Figure 4.2

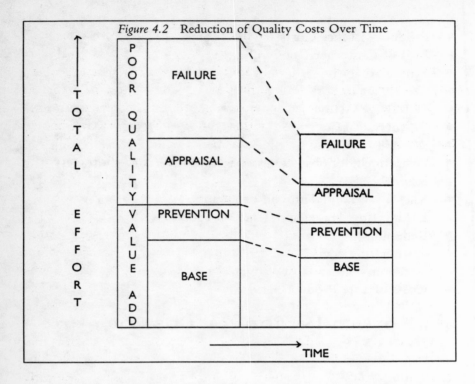

Figure 4.2 Reduction of Quality Costs Over Time

Another danger which may be faced in the early stages is the involvement of accountants. Whilst their help will almost certainly be required down the track, they could possibly provide the main obstacle to progress. The concept of cost estimates is abhorrent to many accountants. However, our initial aim is to prioritise our actions towards improvement and reduction of Quality Costs, and an accuracy of plus or minus 5 per cent or even 10 per cent may be good enough initially. Studies carried out have shown that for many manufacturing organisations, quality related costs account for 25 per cent of turnover; in service industries it is considered to be even higher, at 35 per cent to 40 per cent. This being the case, then for a medium sized company, this may amount to £3 or £4 million, and long discussions centering on absolute accuracy, are unnecessary and another failure cost!

The detail required, and the system used for reporting will vary with each organisation. During the early stages, a rough indication will be sufficient to raise awareness, and motivate management to seek improvements.

Many years ago, we were involved in the early stages of an improvement programme and product rejections were in excess of 20 per cent. At that stage someone remarked that we were in fact 'working one day a week for nothing, merely putting right what we had got wrong last week'. Whilst a cost of quality analysis followed shortly afterwards, this initial statement was sufficient to make everyone more aware of the problem, something that we had come to accept as a part of normal working life.

The system required for the measurement and reporting of quality costs will depend upon the likelihood of them varying within the short term. Very often, they will only change in the medium term because, for example, failure costs are built into costing systems and will not change unless a different approach is used. The problems which lead to these failure costs are unlikely to be easy to solve; if they were, something would already have been done.

It can also be helpful to commence with the collection and analysis of data which already exists within the organisation. This will avoid the necessity for high additional resources during the early stages, and will facilitate the demonstration to senior management of the value of the exercise, and the necessity for its continuation.

It is quite useful to express the total quality cost as a percentage of sales, although this has often been the subject of some debate. The differences in profit and distribution costs between organisations means that this cannot be used as an appropriate comparative measure. In addition, it takes no account of the range of product or services, complexity, market environment or product life-cycle.

In reality, this is a somewhat spurious argument, since the organisation itself has identified a series of opportunities which can be prioritised and actioned in order to reduce the cost of quality, as shown in Figure 4.3.

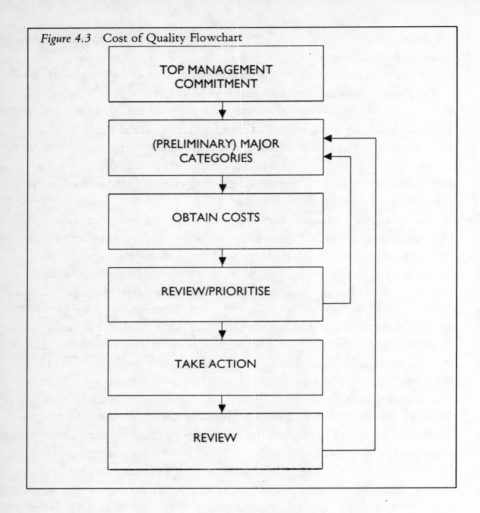

Figure 4.3   Cost of Quality Flowchart

Prioritising the actions necessary following the Cost of Quality Analysis may be usefully undertaken by a Pareto Analysis. This might also indicate cost of quality elements which require further, more detailed, measurement.

To summarise, then, three basic reasons for carrying out the cost of quality exercise are:

● It can stimulate senior management's interest in the opportunities offered by a systematic, structured improvement

programme
- It provides a basis for prioritising projects
- It offers an index of internal effectiveness which can be understood by all employees

4.4 CASE STUDY – TRIPLEX SAFETY GLASS CO. LTD

Triplex Safety Glass Co. Ltd is a part of the Pilkington Group. In 1988 they decided to study the Cost of Quality within their organisation. Since they were major suppliers to Ford Motor Co. Ltd, and had achieved QI status, they enlisted Ford's assistance in the study.

A proper team was formed which agreed that Quality Costs should be broken down into the following categories:

- Prevention
- Appraisal
- Internal Failure
- External Failure

Subsequent discussions, and analysis, further subdivided these categories into more detailed elements. For example, internal failure costs were subdivided into:

- Scrap
- Rework and Repair
- Downgrading

An initial evaluation of the cost of all four categories was made, and teams formed to examine and reduce each element. The results achieved are shown in Figures 4.4 to 4.9.

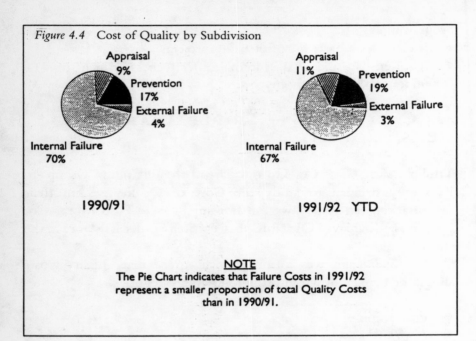

Figure 4.4 Cost of Quality by Subdivision

NOTE
The Pie Chart indicates that Failure Costs in 1991/92
represent a smaller proportion of total Quality Costs
than in 1990/91.

Figure 4.5 Cost of Quality: Quarterly Comparisons

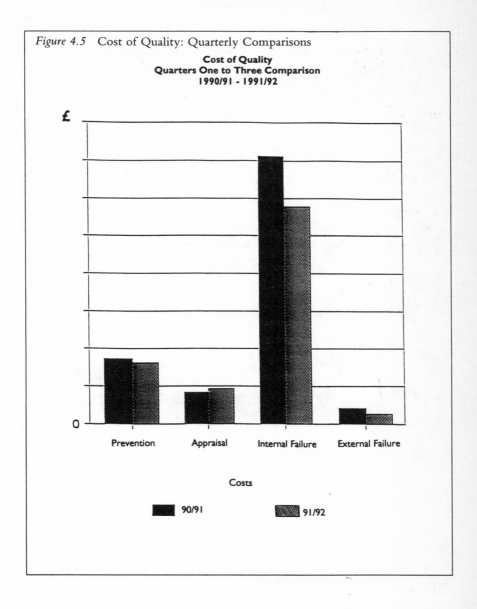

Cost of Quality
Quarters One to Three Comparison
1990/91 - 1991/92

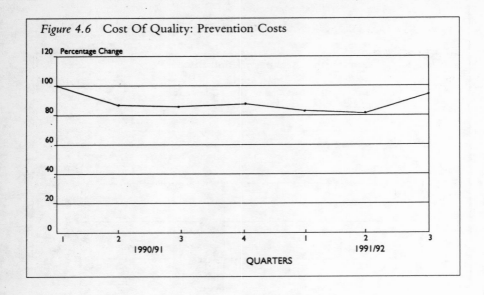

Figure 4.6 Cost Of Quality: Prevention Costs

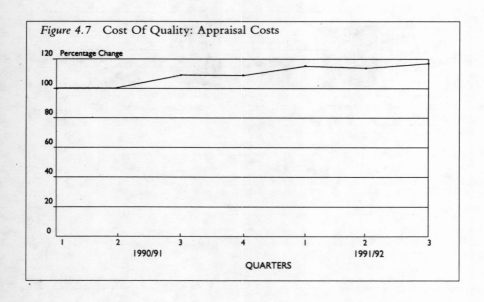

Figure 4.7 Cost Of Quality: Appraisal Costs

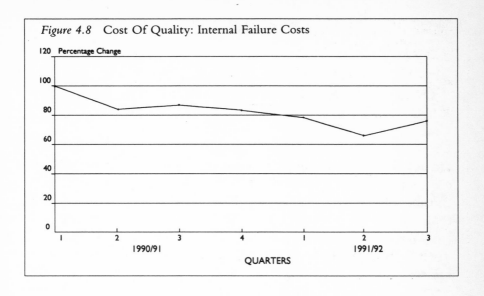

Figure 4.8 Cost Of Quality: Internal Failure Costs

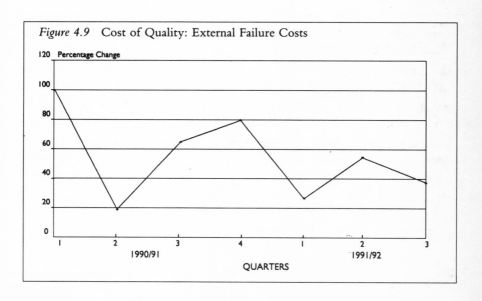

Figure 4.9 Cost of Quality: External Failure Costs

The charts demonstrate what was achieved by categorising the Cost of Quality, and setting up teams to tackle some of the issues raised.

4.5 COST OF QUALITY AS PART OF A TOTAL QUALITY MANAGEMENT PROGRAMME

Cost of Quality is a valuable measurement and improvement tool. However, there is a danger that the organisation will focus on this one issue to the exclusion of other aspects which need to be considered. Many organisations have, in the past, chosen various tools such as BS 5750/ISO 9000, SPC or Taguchi, on an individual basis, and promoted them as sole strategies for improvement.

It is important to understand that identification and measurement of cost of quality elements, will not, of themselves, effect improvement, but will highlight areas for attention. It will depend on those areas, and the subsequent causes which are identified as to how improvement should be sought. For example, causes of unacceptable cost of quality may be inadequate procedures (BS 5750/ISO 9000), poor design (Taguchi) or inadequate control (SPC). For this reason, cost of quality is best utilised as a part of an overall improvement strategy, or Total Quality Management programme. Those involved will then view analysis of cost of quality as a part of the programme, and will be able to put into context the valuable information such an analysis can produce. The culture, or environment, is also an important factor if cost of quality is to be measured and used in a meaningful and effective way, and other initiatives which will be undertaken as part of the Total Quality Management initiative will support the positive attitudes and climate necessary.

5. The Critical Success Factors Approach

5.1 INTRODUCTION

Whilst Cost of Quality provides unification, focus, clarification, building of consensus and prioritisation of areas for improvement within the organisation, and is accordingly useful in the early stages of a quality improvement programme, it can have disadvantages in terms of long-term monitoring of the programme. Reducing everything to cost highlights the arbitrariness of the cost headings, the fact that it is not always possible to get savings through to the bottom line, and the difficulty of monitoring when cost items are really lost in overheads, and we are working with crude estimates. There is a further disadvantage in that concentrating on money, albeit 'artificial' money, can itself destroy the very focus on quality improvement that we are pursuing; it can, alas, all look like another cost cutting programme.

Once one is over the hurdle of starting, there is a better approach for driving a quality improvement programme long-term on a measurement basis, and this is the Critical Success Factors approach. Put simply, the idea is to identify a small number of key indicators that are such that if these are showing satisfactory progress towards targets, the organisation generally will be regarded as being successful on its path of quality improvement. The set needs to be complete in that it, for example, includes Profitability and Cost information, as well as more liberalised aspects associated clearly with quality improvement. But it must not be so extensive that we are unable to see the wood for the trees. Perhaps a half dozen key indicators or Critical Success Factors is ideal. A small enough group, that is, for the monitoring process to be transparent to all those in the organisation, or for progress to be explicit on a single page of graphs, and for everyone to remember the Critical Success Factors. But also a large enough group to span all aspects of the business, and from which all other improvement measures and targets can be derived.

Very often, the approach of Critical Success Factors is used in combination with Quality Policy Deployment (QPD). In Japanese examples of the Critical Success Factors approach, emphasis is often placed upon **Quality** (including service), **Cost** and **Delivery**, (being both accuracy and lead time). These can be summarised by the initials QCD. Japanese companies focus on these throughout the organisation, including the use of mottos expressing appropriate messages on QCD. Having identified these key measures, policy deployment can be used to translate them into the basis for proactive improvement in pursuit of targets on the measures throughout the organisation.

In many Japanese organisations, one of the main Total Quality planning activities is the deployment of the President's Annual Management Policy Plan, which has been developed from the company's long-range and mid-term plans, to all levels of the organisational hierarchy. The plan may be made available to group companies at the beginning of the fiscal year. The deployment is carried out firstly by the plant managers to their respective manufacturing divisions, and then successively the plant manager's policy is deployed by each section departmental manager to his area of responsibility, ultimately through to foreman and operators. The deployment is typically in terms of quality, cost and delivery.

Each plant manager develops his annual policies and improvement targets for every section and department of the plant under his responsibility. He will decide the annual policy for the plant and which key problems need to be tackled in relation to the President's policy. Targets will be based on the long-range business plan, long-range plans for the plant's operation and improvements which need to be made from the previous year's performance, after taking into account an evaluation of the previous year's activities, production scheme etc.

Full discussion and debate will take place with each section manager in relation to their annual policies and plans for departmental activities. Ultimately a final target is agreed, along with a method to reach the objective. The negotiation process between section managers and their superiors is referred to as catch-ball or play-catch. Typically, half-yearly and yearly improvement plans and targets will be set. A similar process then takes place between the section manager and each of his foremen, and ultimately between each foreman and each operator. Records are kept, at all levels, of these agreed improvement actions.

A fixed time period, typically six to eight weeks, is set for the policy management deployment activity to be cascaded down through all organisational levels. This will take place at a set time in the calendar year. With this mechanism in place, control is exercised through diagnosis of problems at management level, discussion of achievements and improvements at conferences on QCD, and day-to-day section management. The Plan-Do-Check-Action cycle (PDCA) may be used extensively in these diagnosis activities.

In addition, auditing may take place by the plant manager on a quarterly basis to verify the progress being made by each section to achieve its improvement objectives. Also, line operators will carry out self-estimation of their achievements against the agreed target. This will form the basis for personal interviews, again at all levels upwards within the organisational hierarchy. All sections report progress to the plant quality assurance department, and these reports form part of the basis for the President's annual audit of the plant.

Typically, some visible manifestations of policy deployment will be available. This helps drive improvement, and within each section there is typically an effort to solve at least two major projects a year. The projects are registered as themes and are derived from the policy deployment process. All of this is in addition to the activity of Quality Control Circles.

Clearly, the system described above has many advantages. It provides a coherence to the improvement programme, focused on the Critical Success Factors of the business, and helps to prioritise action and stop the dilution of efforts over too many projects, as frequently happens in the West. The approach also implies that senior management has a much clearer conception, idea and potential to monitor what is going on in the organisation, and of the barriers and obstacles. This increased clarity and information is also the case for all other employees. Further, the agreement and negotiation processes at each stage imply that consensus or harmony is much more likely to occur, and that the disputes between managerial levels as to who is to blame for not reaching targets is diminished. So, too, are the disputes between differing departments, because parallel sections each know that they have their contribution to make to the next higher level target, which is in itself a unifying force.

To apply such an approach in the West is a big step, requiring much organisational change throughout the business. Where western organisations have gone down this route, typically, they have not thought it possible to go immediately and directly to the whole of the unified, harmonious approach. Instead they have started from part of the normal paraphernalia of the implementation of Total Quality Management – the Mission Statement. Very frequently, western companies establish a Mission Statement as an apparent focus for improvement activities, but then do not provide any direct relationship between the Mission Statement and the various improvement activities. In consequence, the Mission Statement can become a hollow vessel, improvement activities can be unfocused and unprioritised, and the usual one year or two year crisis of confidence or belief can occur in the quality improvement programme.

An alternative approach, utilising some of the best aspects of the Japanese QCD approach, is to translate the Mission Statement into a small set of Critical Success Factors, set targets on these on an annual and longer-term basis, and use them to drive quality improvement throughout the organisation. As such, it is a much smaller step than jumping directly to QCD and policy deployment, but still has the advantage of providing focus for the quality improvement activities within the organisation.

Many western organisations identify Critical Success Factors. However, these very often have the disadvantages of not being clear, quantifiable measures, clearly related to the achievement of the Mission Statement and translatable into focus for all the improvement activities throughout the organisation. Sometimes, also, there are too many of them; twelve is too many, even, for all of us to remember, to think in terms of, to monitor, and not get into wrangles about relative weighting.

If one accepts the Critical Success Factor approach, based on a small set of key performance indicators that reflect the priorities and progress of the business, then it is also necessary to consider their presentation and use. Most effectively, they should be presented and used visually. Simple run charts, with the desired direction of progress, and clear targets for achieved levels by stated points of time, are highly desirable features. This is illustrated in Figure 5.1. An immediate visual impression is presented that helps to see how we are doing. Once established, and the measures validated, any movement in the wrong direction on one of the run charts should be met by immediate management reaction in terms of diagnosis, remedial action, and continued intensive monitoring to resolve the problem. To be used in this way it is important that the Critical Success Factor graphs are compiled on a current, rather than an historic, basis. The graphs should be presented, for example, at monthly board meetings to provide a concise overview of the progress of the organisation.

The Critical Success Factors should always reflect the critical marks of success or failure as identified by the top management team; these are the criteria on which they are running the business and judging it successful. Typically the group of Critical Success Factors may contain customer-orientated measures, as in the case of Japanese companies operating QCD. However, the QCD approach does not, in itself, contain information about the financial performance of the organisation that western management may wish to combine with more customer-focused Critical Success Factor. Typically, therefore, western organisations' Critical Success Factors also contain profit and possibly cost factors, as well as customer-orientated ones.

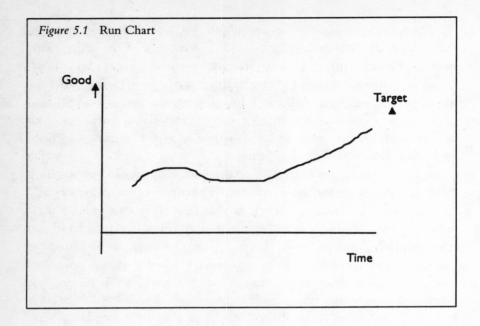

Figure 5.1 Run Chart

Indeed, the approach may be extended to include factors relevant to other stakeholder groups, something to which we return later.

A well known example of this type of approach is that of Florida Power and Light (FPL), the first non-Japanese company to win the Deming Prize, the premier prize for Japanese industry. Florida Power and Light presents a classic example of dedication to achieve its objectives.

5.2 CASE STUDY 1 – HEWLETT-PACKARD, BRISTOL

Hewlett-Packard (HP) is a manufacturer of instruments and computer products with approximately 90,000 employees worldwide, 4,400 of whom work in the UK. Included among HP's UK operations is a division in Bristol named the Computer Peripherals Bristol Division (CPB). CPB employs approximately 500 people and is responsible for designing, manufacturing and marketing small tape drives that are used for storing computer data.

These tape drives are sold on both HP computer systems and those of other manufacturers. The business is global in the sense that CPB exports more than 95 per cent of its production. The major competitors are US and Japanese companies with names like Archive, Exabyte and Sony. To date, CPB has managed to get about a 50 per cent share of the worldwide markets that they have entered.

Based on successful experiences in the Far East, HP has had a corporate initiative to improve the use of total quality control (TQC) throughout the company. There is a widely-held belief that this will lead to better customer service, greater efficiency and high profitability. In Bristol, TQC has been part of the management philosophy since operations started there in 1983. Initially, this took the form of encouraging teams to be established to use the TQC methodology to make process improvements. The earliest successes were in manufacturing areas where tasks were easily identified and data was readily available.

During the last several years, the use of TQC has expanded as a result of management leadership and a drive to apply these concepts in every part of the way Hewlett-Packard run their business. The approach to Total Quality is now based on five areas of Quality Management – the planning process, customer focus, the improvement cycle, process management and people participation. The measurement of key business indicators plays a major role in this system and the way in which the Division is managed. **Primary business measures are organised into business fundamentals tables.** A separate system is used for achieving breakthrough objectives.

Business Fundamentals Tables
The indicators of health of the key processes in CPB are organised into business fundamentals tables. Figure 5.2 shows an example of part of CPB's Division-wide table. The specific example chosen is for product quality, which is measured based on an annualised failure rate (AFR) in the field and by the percentage of units that are dead on arrival (DOA) at the customer site. **Product quality** is one of a dozen critical or key measures of business health at a Divisional level.

Figure 5.2 Business Fundamentals Planning Table

Prepared by: Divison Manager	Date: 25.9.91	Fiscal Year: FY92		Division: DPB	Location/ Department: Divison Wide	
Item	Target/Goals and Limits		Review Period	Data Source	Owner	
CUSTOMER SATISFACTION Quality	AFR <5%	Limit = 8%	Monthly	Warranty Report	Manufacturing Manager	
	DOA Rate <0.5%	Limit = 1%		Major Account Score Card	Manufacturing Manager	

Others include **on-time delivery, manufacturing costs, order rate, shipment revenues, profits, TQC improvement** and **people development**.

Each key measure in the business fundamentals tables has an established **target**, and action limits based on a qualitative feel for when things will be out of control and need management attention. Each measure also has an assigned owner, review period and control document that shows the source data.

These business fundamentals are revised annually. **The targets for most are tightened each year as the Division continues to improve.** For example, Figure 5.3 shows the improvement in AFR (annualised failure rate) that has been made since the time the division started.

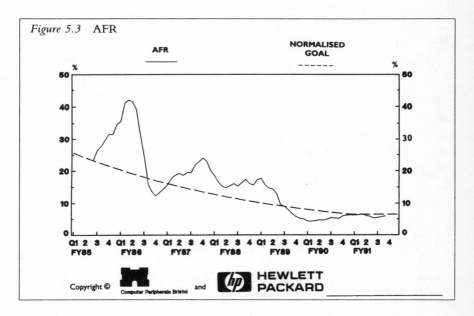

Figure 5.3 AFR

Business fundamentals are **deployed** up and down the organisation as shown in Figure 5.4 and cross linkages are checked for consistency to the extent possible. By going through the process of revising and improving the business fundamentals tables annually for the last five years, they have been increasingly useful and effective. In many areas HP have been able consistently to improve the goals and tighten the action limits on a year-on-year basis.

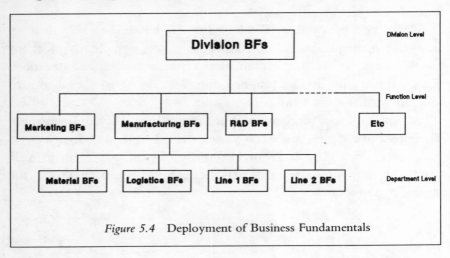

Figure 5.4 Deployment of Business Fundamentals

On a quarterly basis, the state of each of the measures of the top two levels of business fundamentals is rigorously reviewed in a meeting of all of the managers and supervisors (approximately 60 people) in the Division. These reviews are also attended by people from corporate management, by invitation. Each measure that is outside its action limits is analysed to give better understanding of the root of the cause and future implications of this deviation.

Breakthroughs

Business fundamentals are primarily used for stabilising and gradually improving processes. The management and improvement of these processes requires the majority of effort for the people at CPB. A slightly different system is used to manage breakthrough improvements. Examples of potential breakthrough areas might be entering a new market, developing products using a different technology or making a quantum reduction in manufacturing costs. Since most energy is devoted to maintaining and improving existing processes, only a small number (typically three or fewer) of breakthrough objectives are chosen at any particular time.

Figure 5.5 Breakthrough Planning Table

Prepared by: Division Manager	Date: 25.9.91	Fiscal Year: FY92	Division: DPB	Location/Department: Division Wide

SITUATION:
Manufacturing needs to significantly reduce manufacturing cost for product 2 with minimal design changes.

OBJECTIVE	NO	STRATEGY (OWNER)	PERFORMANCE MEASURE
Significantly reduce manufacturing cost for Product 2 while achieving overall goals in business plan.	1.	Significantly reduce variable cost for product 2 by end FY92.	Reduce cost to ≤ $ X by end FY92
	2.	Significantly reduce material costs for Product 2.	Current Breakthrough Material cost $Y $Z
	3.	Significantly improve supplier yields for product 2 and develop/improve key improvement processes to enable meeting 6 sigma program in '94.	1000ppm end Q4 92 100 ppm Q2 93 10 ppm Q4 93 3.4 ppm Q1 94

TARGET/GOAL

$ X extra operating profit in FY93

To implement a breakthrough improvement successfully, one must have a good, clear and well-focused set of strategies. Figure 5.5 shows how these strategies might be laid out on to a Breakthrough Strategy Planning Document. In this case, CPB chose material cost-reduction as the breakthrough objective because of the high influence of material cost reductions on staying competitive in our market place.

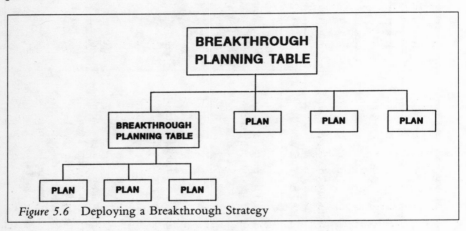

Figure 5.6 Deploying a Breakthrough Strategy

Breakthroughs are deployed based on the activities needed to implement them. This is done by dividing the main strategy into substrategies until one gets to lists of specific implementation items that can be laid out on to a Gantt chart or implementation plan. Figure 5.6 shows a typical hierarchy for deploying a breakthrough strategy. Like business fundamentals, these breakthroughs are reviewed on a regular basis, with quarterly reviews being the most significant.

Comments

The system of quality measurement being used at CPB has become well established because the Division's management has consistently used and improved it as one way in which business progress is tracked. The measures and goals are heavily influenced by what is needed by customers. Those measures have helped focus each employee's mind on what is important for the Division to succeed in a very competitive world. The Division has also tried to be very careful not to over-measure and over-analyse. It is extremely easy to create bureaucracy that suffocates any potential benefits. Over time they have found it better to reduce the frequency of reviews and make each review more in-depth to look at problems and root causes. The Division expects to continue to improve on the systems that they have already established.

CASE STUDY 2 – MARCONI DEFENCE SYSTEMS LIMITED (MDSL)

A slightly different, but related, approach was taken by Marconi Defence Systems Ltd. Having established the Managing Director's commitment to a company-wide TQM programme, a phased plan was created and put into operation. During the initial stages, the Top Teams were identified and two-day workshops were run.

Resulting from these initial workshops were several management assignments, all of which were aimed at establishing the perceived 'health' of the company. What sort of company did the teams think they were? How did their customers perceive them? What did they think they needed to address for MDSL to become the world class company they envisaged?

In parallel with these assignments the Top Team also prepared draft proposals for the company's Mission and Philosophy Statements. These submissions were subsequently collated and, during several Team sessions, were broken down into the key and common elements. Using these key points, the Team put together an agreed pair of statements which crystallised where, as a company, they wanted to go (The Mission) and how, as a company, they wanted to get there (The Philosophy). This vital stage completed, the Statements then formed the backdrop against which the subsequent 'Diagnostic Reviews' could take place.

The various other management assignments produced data which was collated by a small TQM co-ordination group. Each **Critical Success Factor** (CSF) submission was 'checked' against a set of 'entry criteria' and against the Mission and Philosophy Statements to ensure suitability.

Those submissions which met all criteria were then honed to provide the Critical Success Factors. These formed the basis of the ensuing Diagnostic Reviews and were the distillation of all successful submissions.

The company is located at two main sites – Portsmouth and Stanmore. Because of the size of each it had been decided to hold two Diagnostic workshops, one on each site, using a cross-site mix of people. Each Team consisted of between twelve and sixteen Executive Managers. Only nine of the original fifteen CSFs were to be dealt with, and these were selected during the reviews, the remainder being put on hold. The Teams were broken down into Assignment Groups each consisting of about four people, and using brainstorming sessions and subsequent use of 'How–How' explosion charts, they plotted those elements of each CSF which needed to be addressed in order to reach the company goal.

The activity proved to be extremely useful and searching; a surprisingly large number of elements/processes were identified for each CSF. The subsequent analysis by each Team identified up to six **Critical Processes** (CPs) applicable to their allocated CSF. Examples of the CSF's and subsequent Critical Process Summary Charts are shown in Figures 5.7–5.11.

Figure 5.7   Critical Success Factor I

PEOPLE
ACTIVELY
COMMITTED TO
EXCELLENCE

CRITICAL SUCCESS FACTOR NO. 1

Both Teams

GOAL

Reduce Product Time to Market cycles below our competitors'.

CRITICAL ASSUMPTIONS

We can obtain or assess competitors' and comparable firms' cycle times.

TYPICAL INDICATOR

Graph of Cost-then-Income versus Time.

Marconi
Defence Systems

Figure 5.8   Critical Success Factor II

**PEOPLE
ACTIVELY
COMMITTED TO
EXCELLENCE**

CRITICAL SUCCESS FACTOR NO. 5
Stanmore Team

GOAL

Outstanding responsiveness to Customers' Enquiries.

CRITICAL ASSUMPTIONS

We can obtain or assess competitors' and comparable firms' responsiveness, and compare with our own.

TYPICAL INDICATOR

Bid win/lose ratio (or success rate) in terms of numbers of bids and cost.

Marconi
Defence Systems

Figure 5.9 Critical Success Factor III

  PEOPLE
ACTIVELY
COMMITTED TO
EXCELLENCE

CRITICAL SUCCESS FACTOR NO. 11
Production Team

GOAL

Consistently Make Deliveries to Contract Requirement.

CRITICAL ASSUMPTIONS

We know the requirement.
We can record the achievement.

TYPICAL INDICATORS

Comparison Charts.
Volume of Concessions.

Marconi
Defence Systems

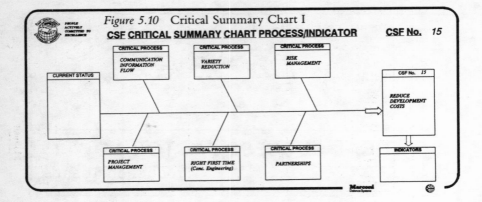

Figure 5.10 Critical Summary Chart I

The outputs from the Diagnostic Reviews were collated and a matrix compiled of Critical Success Factors against Critical Processes. This was to identify any Critical Processes which affected more than one CSF. In this way, the company could prioritise the attack and ensure maximum return for effort expended. This was to allow their 'Fast Track' improvement programme to be determined and agreed.

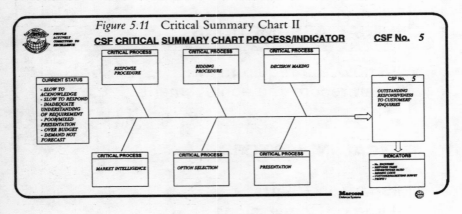

Figure 5.11 Critical Summary Chart II

The total matrix is shown in Figures 5.12 and 5.13. This was again distilled ex-committee to arrive at the top line 'Hit List' against which sponsors were chosen to head up the Task teams to tackle the Critical Processes and the ensuing problems. All of these processes have cross-site implications.

Figure 5.12 CSF Critical Process Matrix I

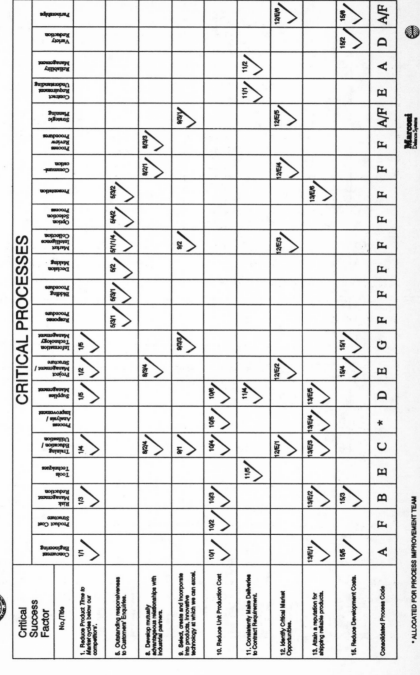

Figure 5.13 CSF Critical Process Matrix II

CRITICAL PROCESSES

Critical Success Factor No./Title	A Design for Manufacture, Producability and Customer Satisfaction	B Management of Commercial and Technical Risk	C Continuous Improvement of Human Resources Capability	D Supplier Management	E Project Management	F Information Management	G Winning Business
1. Reduce Product *Time to Market* cycles below our competitors'.	HH 1/1	HH 1/3	HH 1/4	HH 1/5	HH 1/2		HH 1/5
5. Outstanding responsiveness to Customers' Enquiries.						HH 5/3/1 HH 5/4/2 HH 5/2 HH 5/3/2 HH 5/1/1/4	
6. Develop mutually advantageous relationships with industrial partners.			HH 8/2/4	HH 8/E/1	HH 8/3/4 HH 8/3/3		
9. Select, create and incorporate into products, innovative technology at which we can excel.	HH 9/3/1		HH 9/1			HH 9/2	HH 9/3/3
10. Reduce Unit Production Cost	HH 10/1	HH 10/3	HH 10/4	HH HH 10/8	HH 10/E	HH 10/2	
11. Consistently Make Deliveries to Contract Requirement.	HH 11/2			HH 11/4	HH 11/1 HH 11/5		
12. Identify Critical Market Opportunities.			HH 12/E/1		HH 12/E/2		HH 12/E/3 HH 12/E/5 HH 12/E/4 HH 12/E/6
13. Attain a reputation for shipping reliable products.	HH 13/E/1	HH 13/E/2	HH 13/E/3	HH 13/E/4		HH 13/E/5	
15. Reduce Development Costs.	HH 15/5 HH 15/2 HH 15/6	HH 15/3		HH 15/2	HH 15/4	HH 15/E/2	HH 15/1
Task Team Leader	Div. Director	Production Director	Personnel Director	Commercial Director	Div. Director	Information Tech. Director	Div. Director

Marconi Defence Systems

Today MDSL has identified its Mission and Philosophy, it has identified the Critical Success Factors which have to be achieved and the Critical Processes to be improved in order to achieve them. It is believed that the benefits gained by local process improvements over the preceding years will prove to be only the tip of the iceberg that is about to be 'melted down' with the Task Team operation.

The company believes that there are major benefits to employing multi-discipline, cross-functional teams; this is clearly the way to break down barriers, provide full understanding of all processes and achieve total process capability. Marconi Defence Systems Ltd offers as a slogan:

UNDERSTANDING THE PROCESS IS THE KEY TO CONTINUOUS IMPROVEMENT AND A SECURE FUTURE

CASE STUDY 3 – EAST MIDLANDS ELECTRICITY (EME)

The first author of this book is East Midlands Electricity's Professor of Quality Management at the Nottingham Trent University, and it is natural to include East Midlands Electricity as a case study. Prior to privatisation, East Midlands Electricity Board was a pathfinder amongst the regional electricity distribution companies in its attitude to Customer Care and to Total Quality. A major Total Quality Management training programme was introduced and a Quality Development Department established. The head of this department, the Quality Development Manager, reports directly to the Managing Director of the plc. This indicates the importance of the activity from the viewpoint of the company.

Following a visit from the US quality expert Myron Tribus, the company established a Quality Council, to which the Quality Development Manager provided the secretariat. As a result of the development of an ongoing consulting, research and training relationship between Professor Bendell and his team at the Nottingham Trent University and EME, Professor Bendell became the East Midland Electricity's Professor of Quality Management in

September 1991. As well as public activities, his brief is to implement and develop quality techniques and practices within East Midlands Electricity. Both East Midlands Electricity and the Nottingham Trent University are key players in the East Midlands Quality Club, which is chaired by Professor Bendell and currently has some 45 member organisations within the East Midlands.

East Midlands Electricity's vision is simply to be the best electricity company in the U.K. In working towards this the company recognises five groups of stakeholders, that is people with an interest in, and a relationship with, the company. These are:

- **customers**, who give the company their business and expect the company to satisfy their needs;
- **investors**, who provide the company with the funds to operate the business and expect a return on their investment;
- **employees**, who provide their skill and commitment and who expect remuneration and appreciation;
- **suppliers**, who provide the company with goods and services and who expect orders, payments and understanding;
- **the community**, who constitute the environment in which the company exists and works and to whose development the company contributes.

The existence of the stakeholder concept within East Midlands Electricity introduces additional complications to the development of the Critical Success Factor approach. This approach is now being investigated within the Electricity Division of the company, which is the largest of the four divisions of the new plc. The concept is to build a hierarchy of easily understandable measures which at the top level are represented in one page of run-graphs, which on its own summarises each of the stakeholder groups and the two-way relationship between the company and that stakeholder group. Behind that top-level summary there would be, for each stakeholder group, a top-level summary page based on run-graphs and contour diagrams etc., which again represent for that stakeholder group a set of top-level summaries of the performance in relation to the Critical

Success Factors. Behind each of those second pages could be a set of lower-level measures, again breaking down the higher level information into information for parts of the business, market categories or lower summary indexes. Illustrations, but not actuals, are shown in Figures 5.14–5.15.

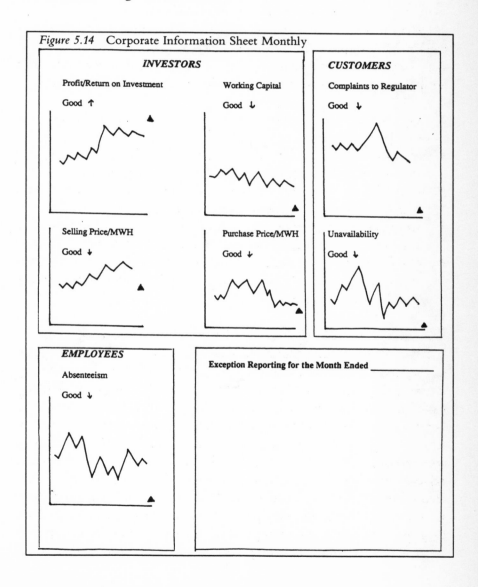

Figure 5.14   Corporate Information Sheet Monthly

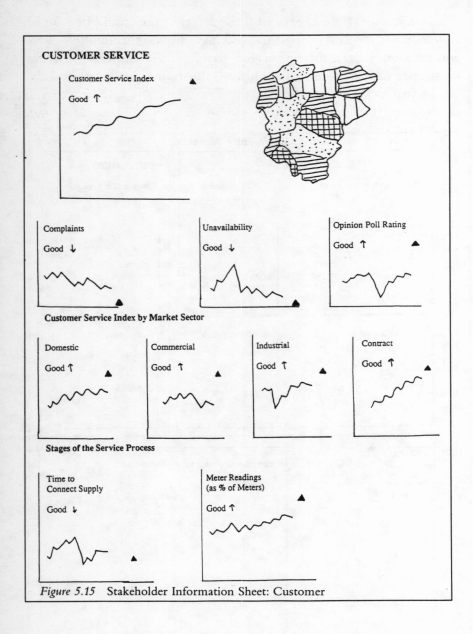

Figure 5.15 Stakeholder Information Sheet: Customer

The intention would be that this type of information could eventually be used by the Divisional board for routine monitoring and decision making. There is some way to go, still, in development to achieve that objective. Currently, a Working Group chaired by the Divisional Operations Director, Chris Hutt, is identifying and developing suitable measures based on internal investigation and surveys of stakeholder groups.

6. What to Measure and When – the Process, Not the Outputs

6.1 INTRODUCTION

For measurement to be useful for driving quality improvement, it must be relevant to customer needs and wants. It must be current, not historic, and it must be on the process and not wait for the outputs, which may be too late.

The age of the large historic data system is, perhaps, coming to an end. Such systems frequently fail to tell us anything about the actuality of the current situation, concentrating instead on historic information. What is measured may not be relevant to the satisfaction of the customer, but may be collected purely for operational requirements within the supplying organisation. Measuring outputs implies that whatever may go wrong, has already gone wrong. We are reacting too late. It would be much better to react during the process internal to the organisation, rather than when the product or service is supplied to the customer.

Total Quality Management, itself, is about clarifying organisations, about relationships, and about purposes. A crucial aspect of this is to see clearly how internal business activities relate to the final satisfaction of the customer. This is the only way we can concentrate effort where it matters, in supporting the customer requirements and needs, and streamline activity elsewhere, where activities have little value–added to the requirements of the customer.

In carrying out this analysis of our internal business activities to support satisfaction of the customer needs, the crucial concept is that of the **process**. Processes are not just manufacturing paths or conveyor belts; they represent business operations, by which we satisfy customer needs.

What is a process? A process can be defined as a mechanism by which inputs are transformed into outputs. For a business process, outputs may include product, services, materials, and procedures that differ from the original output. For example, in passing an invoice for payment there are various stages that need to be gone through. It has been estimated that on some occasions this may involve up to 350 different stages or process steps. These steps, typically, belong to different personnel, or different departments and as such there tends to be no process owner to champion the service to the customer throughout the organisation. It is not surprising, therefore, that most problems arise where there are hand-overs between one functional responsibility and another, owing to poor communication, or unclear responsibilities. There is a clear need to develop process owners, in order to be sure that the customer requirements are met.

6.2 IDENTIFYING, DESCRIBING AND ANALYSING PROCESSES

Concepts of internal business processes relate to the concept of customer/supplier chains, which is quite common in Total Quality terminology. Primary processes related to the organisation's core business relate to meeting external customer needs. Such a need may be met by a series of internal customer/supply transactions, whereby each of the players who will eventually contribute to the satisfaction of the need of the external customer contribute and pass their work, whether in physical form or in concept, on to the next stage in the chain – their internal customer. The internal customer then becomes an internal supplier to the next internal customer. Ultimately, the final customer is served by the last of the internal suppliers.

Looking at organisations in this way creates a revolution in thinking. In terms of measurement, clearly crucial measurements should be taken internally to the processes themselves, once they have been identified, in order to ensure ultimate customer satisfaction. Merely measuring the end output to customers or customer satisfaction would be too late and not very effective a control.

There is no reason at all why most of the concepts of measuring and monitoring that have been historically developed, cannot be applied to this concept of business processes, whether they are aspects of the core business or subsidiary processes, existing to support core business activities in an indirect way.

How then should the business go about identifying, describing and analysing processes? The identification stage is time-consuming, repetitive and sometimes fraught. As with so much else in Total Quality Management, the basic technique is to assemble a group who between them have an overall concept of the process and to extract from them local information, to enable the process to be adequately described. In carrying out this operation, flowcharting is extremely valuable, since it provides a visual, and yet documented, version of the process being described. Once a draft flowchart section is put up as a speculation on how that stage of the process works, it becomes much easier for other members of the team to identify mistakes in conception, in the description of the internal processes, and also to identify negative paths, where what should happen has not happened, and therefore remedial action is actually taken.

Such negative paths are among the major issues associated with the process view of organisations. The unusual document that requires some particular thought, or enquiry of others, which stays in the corner of a desk for an indefinite period, is a classic example of this type of problem. Unfortunately, such an unusual document may well experience these sorts of problems at various stages in its transition through the organisation, leading to enormous delay and confusion for the customer waiting upon service. Indeed, when something starts to go wrong within an organisation, processes have often not been established to deal with these complexities, and human intervention in an intelligent fashion is deemed to be necessary. No process documentation may exist under these circumstances.

With a flowchart, then, problems and bottlenecks can be quickly identified. If there are conflicts or delays between the different departments, anomalies in the procedure will also be identified.

If there is a perceived time problem in getting the product or service delivery through all process stages, it is worth involving a 'process engineer' to identify the times that a product should be at each stage of the process, then compare it to the actual. It may be that the delays are due to the process time constraints; it may also be that the product spends 90 per cent of its process time waiting for the next stage. All of these aspects need to be investigated, analysed and improved upon.

One approach may be to establish an overall process owner and a process improvement team with a formal support role. In order to describe each major process, it is helpful to identify a process owner. The use of a process owner clarifies the ambiguities for those who think they own the process. The individual should be given full responsibility for the process and may have to be given responsibility for cutting across organisational lines. The process owner's duties are to ensure that proper focus is placed on the entire process across all organisational structures, to drive process improvements and to ensure that all changes to the process have an overall positive effect. The first duty of the process owner will be to define its boundary. Within the boundary should be everything from the point where the first supplier provides input into the process, to the point at which the customer is supplied with the output.

The process owner must be someone who is motivated to make the total process operate efficiently. It may be the person who has most to gain or lose by the success of the process. Process ownership does not necessarily constitute a full-time job: when the process is working efficiently the person should have more time because less time is spent chasing problems.

The process owner will need the support of a process improvement team, the members of which will be dictated by the boundary of the process. The primary responsibility of the team may be initially to develop either a flow diagram of the process or Process Deployment Flowcharts. Part of this exercise should include a process walk-through study, where an individual or small team walk through the process from start to finish. From this, anomalies, possible delays or opportunities for items/customers to be lost, if they fall out of the normal process, will be encountered. The adequacy of on-line checks (equipment, service or product), poor operating conditions or procedures will also be identified. Where necessary the introduction of feed back loops or the introduction of measurement points can be recommended. It may be that the process can be streamlined or that more control could be introduced by, for example, restructuring production into units or teams. This latter approach has been used in companies such as Honeywell and Coats Viyella.

Traditionally, the output of the process receives attention, because the emphasis in the past has been on inspection or detection, rather than prevention. The chapter on the Cost of Quality has demonstrated that this is a very expensive way forward. However, by ensuring that the process is in control, that the inputs are always capable of meeting the requirements of the process, and that the process will only produce correct product, then these detection costs and rectification costs will be reduced.

In this model of things, then, process control is also important for monitoring, and for forecasting of eventual cost, time scale, and problem handling.

To define a process, the boundaries must first be set down. These should include everything from the first supplier that supplies input to the process, to the point at which the customer is supplied with the output.

For example, in Figure 6.1 we show a simplified typing process. At the print-out stage, there might be both header and continuation paper. At the memo stage, this may be written, taped or dictated.

The secretary may have to find the address, and so on. All these possible variations to be initiated are called subprocesses. It is important to realise that each organisation will have a different set of subprocesses depending on its own work practices, but by adopting standard processes throughout an organisation staff interchangeability and standardisation between different departments is much easier to achieve.

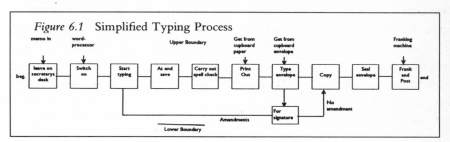

Figure 6.1 Simplified Typing Process

To identify a process, then, we must look at the provision of product or service to a customer and the steps to provide it, ask how it is delivered, and follow the work-flow through the organisation, from first input stage. To describe a process, some sort of flowcharting is particularly useful, or we can rely on procedure writing such as is common in Quality Assurance systems and implementing ISO 9000. To analyse processes, we must now look at those flowcharts, at the negative paths and the boundaries, and all other aspects, in order to identify deficiencies. These may include 'holes' in the process when certain particular peculiar circumstances occur, unnecessary repetitive operations, clear organisational inefficiencies, inherent lack of customer contact, over–complicated procedures of a bureaucratic nature, and lack of ownership.

6.3 PROCESS DEPLOYMENT FLOWCHARTS

In Figure 6.2 we show a simple illustration of the use of Process Deployment Flowcharts in order to illustrate the various symbols used in their construction. The essential aspects of Process Deployment Flowcharting is that the horizontal dimension of the flowchart is used to define the cast of characters, and standard symbols are used throughout the flowchart to facilitate easy understanding. With these two features in place, this type of chart is invaluable for describing processes, for facilitating proceduralisation such as in gaining certification to ISO 9000, for clarifying issues about cost of quality and for identifying measurement points in the internal business processes, as well as just seeing those business processes unambiguously, probably for the first time.

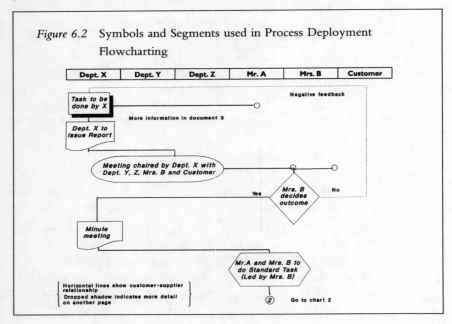

Figure 6.2 Symbols and Segments used in Process Deployment Flowcharting

In Figure 6.2 we can see that a task initiated by department X is described in more detail in Document 3, but is carried out in consultation with Mr A. Once a task has been completed, department X issues a report, depicted by a sheaf of papers, and then calls a meeting with department Y, department Z and in collaboration with Mrs B and the customer. The meeting is denoted by the sausage shape. Following the meeting Mrs B initiates action and decides the outcome. If the outcome is a positive one, department X minutes the meeting and Mrs B, together with Mr A, do a standard task, led by Mrs B. However, if the outcome is a negative one, then the ball passes back to department X to do the initial task again, in consultation with Mr A.

The usefulness of this particular approach can be seen in Figure 6.3. This shows a Process Deployment Flowchart that has been used to debug a simple invoicing procedure. This is taken from one of Services Ltd's clients, and shows how the simple approach of Process Deployment Flowcharts enables immediate clarification of poorly understood processes.

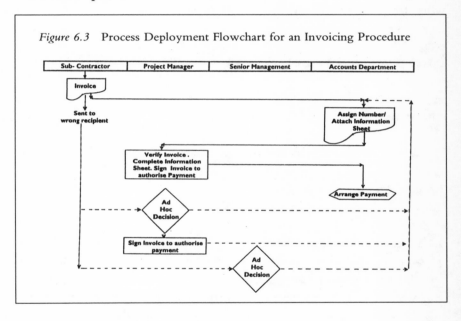

Figure 6.3 Process Deployment Flowchart for an Invoicing Procedure

Here invoices are raised by a subcontractor. However, instead of sending the invoice to the Accounts Department, some subcontractors send them incorrectly to the Project Manager or Senior Management. This arose in the particular client organisation because a sub-contractor had been first identified and selected by the Project Manager or a Senior Manager, and had not then received explicit instructions to send all invoices to the Accounts Department. The company's procedure was to assign a number and attach an information sheet to all incoming invoices, when they arrived at the

Accounts Department. This also enabled the Accounts Department to forecast future cash requirements. Invoices were then passed to the Project Manager for verification, and to complete the information sheet and sign in order to authorise payment. Although a simple procedure, it frequently went wrong when the invoices arrived first at the Project Manager or Senior Manager, before the Accounts Department. They became lost in the system and considerable delays resulted. This was further confused on occasion by inappropriate signature by the Project Manager, in an attempt to circumvent the procedures he knew to exist when the invoice reached the Accounts Department.

6.4 Using process Deployment Flowchart to Analyse the Process

In looking at a process there are a number of aspects that can be considered.

1. Where do the inputs for the activities come from? Can they be more suitably located and how are they identified?
2. Is the condition of the input acceptable, and who controls it? What documentation currently controls the activities and is it adequate?
3. Does the documentation system cover all aspects of each activity? How are the employees trained for these activities, and was the training adequate?
4. Analyse how the operator or employee carrying out a task is able to assess that he or she is conducting the activity correctly.
5. What are the typical faults that the employee receives or has to face? Are the employees aware of the faulty work they pass on to the next internal customer and do they even know who their customer is?
6. Identify the nature of problems that the employee experiences with each activity and extract, and clarify any suggestions they have to improve the activities.
7. Identify what, if anything, makes that activity difficult to accomplish.

8. Identify what is dissatisfying about carrying out the job activities.

This kind of analysis of the internal business process is not only very useful or essential in gaining a full understanding of the process, but also provides a lot of opportunities for improvement and identification of problems from the workplace itself. It can also provide valuable information on such key areas as training, the working environment, process weaknesses and strengths, together with possible measurement points. The walk-through process, also, highlights routines that may or may not be within the boundaries of the process, so that definition of the process is clarified.

A good procedure for analysing processes is as follows:

1. Identify and label the process and assign a single process owner and the team that he or she is going to cooperate with.
2. Define the boundaries of the process.
3. Document the process flow, preferably by the Process Deployment Flowchart.
4. Define control points and measurements.
5. Communicate and implement.
6. Measure and assess.
7. Identify improvement opportunities.

6.5 PROCESS MEASUREMENT

Various types of measurement can be used in relation to processes. **Effectiveness** measures how good is the output from the process. An aspect of this includes **accuracy** i.e. is it correct or not correct, if so by how much. Others are **reliability** i.e. how many times it is correct; **timeliness** i.e. it could be correct all the time but always late, and if so by how much; **volume** i.e. it may always be correct and on time, but the customer may perhaps only get half the required volume. Other aspects are **ease of use, completeness, capability**

119

and **efficiency**. Efficiency tells us how well the resources are utilised. In addition there is **adaptability**: how well the process can adjust to special requirements or long term change, for example an environmental condition, ageing or even the ability for staff to change.

Whilst the above aspects of measurement are appropriate at the end of the process, it is more important to use them at the end of process stages, internally to the process itself. Good measurement points are on horizontal lines on the Process Deployment Flowchart, since these represent customer/supplier relationships. Inaccuracy, unreliability, lack of timeliness or incorrect volume on these relationships can eventually cause dissatisfaction to the ultimate customer. Equally, poor ease of use, incompleteness, poor capability, bad efficiency or unadaptability at these internal process stages will ultimately represent a poor level of service to the customer.

Before introducing improvement activities, measurements should be established to provide a benchmark to measure the effectiveness of the improvement process itself. Measurement should also provide feedback, giving an individual or group the opportunity to improve. Traditionally, there are few measurement points for office and managerial staff, though these staff, traditionally, are good at identifying problems that they encounter.

With process measurement it is important to define measurement points that will evaluate the output as close as possible to the source of the errors. The errors may be identified by the process improvement team, or the actual department, during a brainstorming session, or by other means. It is important that realistic procedures are used, or, if it is difficult to measure, that a short duration is imposed, a week, a shift etc. in order to cause minimum disruption.

Measurement and monitoring may be either quantitative or qualitative. While quantitative is preferred, qualitative may be the only option.

Generally, it should be possible to establish feedback loops, and allow individuals to correct parameters within their control. We may, for example, provide word processor operators with spellchecks prior to printing documents and ensure that they are used. This information is also needed to allow management to invest in equipment, training or change procedures to prevent the errors from recurring.

If this feedback cycle can be built into the process, two savings are made:

1. Employees do not continue to make the errors.
2. Additional resources are not added to an already effective system.

As a guide, six levels of process evaluation have been defined.

- **Level one** is world-class.
- **Level two** is error free, where the process is highly effective and efficient.
- **Level three** represents an efficient process that is streamlined.
- **Level four** represents the effective process that is systematically measured, streamlining has started and the customer expectations are met.
- **Level five** represents a situation where process design is understood and operates according to documented procedures.
- The lowest level, **Level six,** is where the process status has not been evaluated and is unknown.

Tools used for evaluating processes include many that have been dealt with elsewhere within this book. Examples are Quality Function Deployment, Benchmarking, Cost of Quality, Structural Analysis etc.

In carrying out process analysis, not all information gathered will be used by everyone. It is important that when the measurement points are evaluated the final reporting should be considered. Figure 6.4 illustrates some aspects of organisational reporting. Each of the horizontal lines represent a filter, where information is gathered, but not necessarily passed on. At Director level, each Director is measuring quality and other issues relating to them. This may all be drawn from data provided by senior management. These business-wide quality measures are macro-measures that reveal the general performance of the business against objectives. These measures are the broadest in scope and are placed at the top of the pyramid.

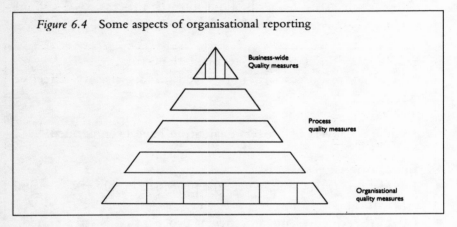

Figure 6.4   Some aspects of organisational reporting

Process quality measures are the horizontal layers gathering data through several vertical layers (functions), summarising it for one final customer. Process quality measures are the indicators that ensure horizontal work activity consistently meets requirements, that are continuously improved. The organisational quality measures are again specific, corresponding to discrete organisational departments and depicting how each meets its quality objectives.

6.6 CASE STUDY – COATS VIYELLA APPAREL CMT DIVISION

As part of a Cost of Quality exercise covering the design, manufacture and sale of ladieswear and childrenswear, the design function was selected as an area to study for a Cost of Quality evaluation. A flowchart was constructed to show the process of design throughout the season, and the production of samples was highlighted as the most problematic area. The Process Deployment Flowchart is shown in Figure 6.5.

This flowchart clarified a process which was not even defined previously. Negative feedback loops in particular were a surprise, and the diagram forms a basis for subsequent process changes concentrated on where there were greatest problems. Here, brainstorming was utilised in order to identify improvement.

The CMT Division of Coats Viyella, based at Mansfield, have been undertaking a Total Quality programme for the last two years.

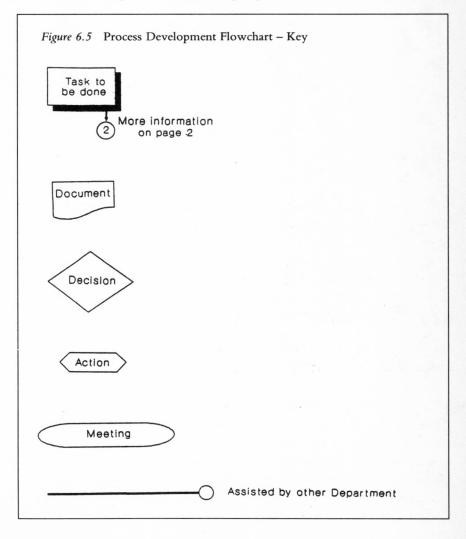

Figure 6.5 Process Development Flowchart – Key

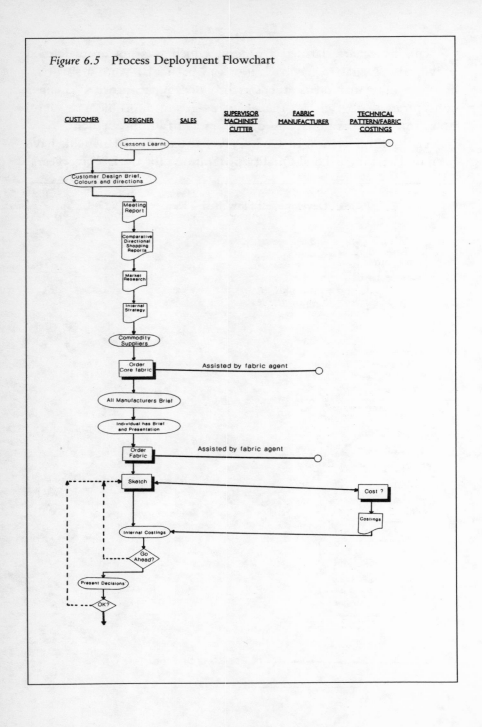

Figure 6.5 Process Deployment Flowchart

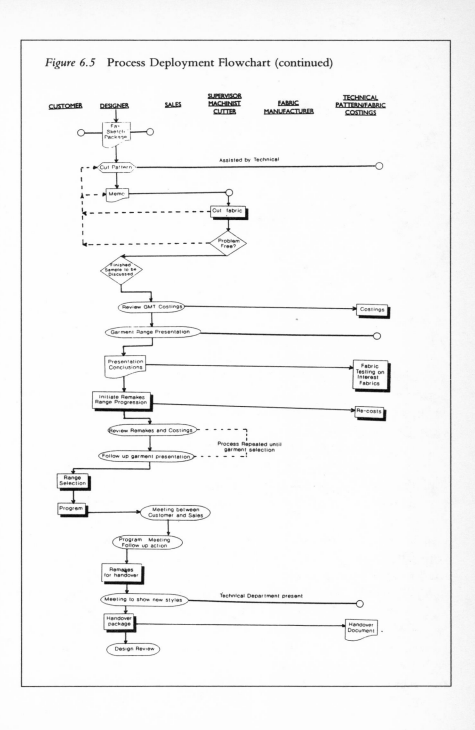

Figure 6.5 Process Deployment Flowchart (continued)

7. How Does Your Organisation Measure Up? – Benchmarking

7.1 INTRODUCTION

Where do your business targets come from? And how does your performance compare with the competition? Can you be sure that the improvements that you are making will bring your performance closer to the market leaders – or are they widening the gap?

Like Cost of Quality programmes and the Critical Success Factors approach discussed in previous chapters, benchmarking is a tool that can be used for identifying improvement areas and for prioritising and monitoring improvement activity. Beyond that, though, it is a methodology for objectively determining the business targets that an organisation must aim for and achieve if it is to compete effectively. As such, it is often used to establish the targets used in the Critical Success Factors approach.

Today, for many businesses, competition is on the world stage and, in the critical areas selected, the only sensible goals are 'world best practice'. For many other companies, competing in smaller arenas, the targets may not always be as stringent but the need for realistic goal-setting is just as important. Benchmarking is a method for making sure that the targets aimed for are relevant to market demands and not arbitarily established by finger in the air or extrapolation from last year's achievements. The technique is equally applicable in manufacturing and service organisations and in the public and private sectors.

Benchmarking is a process for driving continuous improvement – by constant effort to close the gap between your performance in selected areas, and the best performance that you can find to measure against in the same areas. In Robert C. Camp's 1989 book, *Benchmarking: The Search for Industry Best Practices that Lead to Superior Performance*, he cites the definition put forward by David T Kearns, CEO of the Xerox Corporation as:

> . . . *the continuous process of measuring products, services and practices against the toughest competitors or those companies recognized as industry leaders.*

Making comparisons with competitors is not a new idea. Acquiring data about how one's competitors are performing, what their product range comprises, what prices they are able to command and perhaps their operating methods, has always been part of the marketing function's modus operandi. Benchmarking today, however, is much more sophisticated than a furtive, mainly reactive, short-term data-gathering exercise. Instead, it is a highly-respected proactive management tool which is increasingly being used to identify and focus improvement activities with the goal of international competitiveness.

The Japanese, perhaps, made it into an art form. Starting in the late 1950s, they visited many thousands of companies around the world, mainly in America and western Europe, specifically to absorb ideas that they could adopt, adapt and improve upon for their own manufacturing processes. They investigated western products and processes to understand the good and bad features and then built superior alternatives at a lower cost. They also transferred good practices and technology used in one business area to a completely different area, driven by a commitment to company-wide continuous improvement.

The Xerox Corporation in America adopted a similarly vigorous approach in 1979, motivated by a rapidly diminishing market share. Their competitors were able to sell products more cheaply than Xerox could make them. To understand why, the product features and performance capabilities of competitive machines were rigorously evaluated and Xerox were also able to investigate the practices of Fuji-Xerox in Japan. The improvement opportunities identified and put into place resulted in a swift turnaround for Xerox's fortunes and led to best practice benchmarking becoming a central part of their business strategy. Xerox, and Rank Xerox Ltd in the UK, are generally recognised as the leaders in the benchmarking field in the western hemisphere.

Following the lead given by Xerox, the technique is increasingly being used in America and it has become a qualifying condition for companies aiming for the prestigious Malcolm Baldrige Award for Quality. In this country, 'benchmarking' has become the latest buzz word. Increasingly, over the last two years, it has become almost impossible to pick up a magazine about quality or management without reference to the process. Conferences and seminars are held, articles are written, training is offered – and of course there are the fact-finding tours to the Far East.

How much benchmarking, though, is actually being done? Certainly the larger multi-nationals are two or three years down the track, especially if the parent company is American. The automotive giants and many electronics companies are similarly committed to it. There are different levels of benchmarking, though (see below), and very few organisations, if any, seem to have gone as far as the highly-structured, formalised approach adopted by Xerox. There is some lip-service paid to the process. Perhaps some of this results from a lack of knowledge of what is really involved; perhaps some results from the high front-end investment coupled with the long learning curve and delayed payback.

For companies where attention is focused inward, perception of what can be achieved, and what is being achieved, is limited. There is a limit, too, to the improvement that can be made to existing processes and practices; the 'law of diminishing returns' applies and it is difficult to sustain motivation. There is a need for the injection of new concepts and new philosophies and for awareness of innovative practices and revolutionary approaches. Benchmarking can provide all of these plus the stimulus to adopt them for your business. It is outward-looking and customer-focused and allows organisations to get ahead of the game rather than being forced reluctantly to try to catch up with the pack.

7.2 Doing it

Before we go through the steps in the benchmarking process it is necessary to make some general observations. There can be many problems and pitfalls. Not least are the usual ones encountered when companies decide to 'implement' the other aspects of Total Quality Management.

Commitment from the top is absolutely essential if the approach is to be successful and if improvements are to follow from the comparative measuring exercise. Times vary greatly, but generally, the research activity can take between six and 18 months to complete and the level of resource that needs to be committed can be very high. Then the hard part – making the improvements – begins. Benchmarking is no quick fix with instant payback; unless senior management show patience and take leadership for the change process, the whole activity is likely to become another 'flavour of the month' – resulting in frustration and apathy.

There must be a belief in the need to change. This belief is likely to be reinforced when comparisons with market leaders are made, but it is management's responsibility to generate enthusiasm for improvements and to overcome resistance to change throughout the organisation. Benchmarking is a tool to help the change process and not the preserve of a few elite specialists. The people who will be asked to make changes following the benchmarking exercise must be involved with the process from the beginning. Their input will help to prevent silly mistakes being made during the study and they will recognise the need for improvement when the comparisons are made.

If their first introduction to the benchmarking exercise comes from the analysis and consists of 'Company X can produce twice as much as you can in half the time' without any reference to how, then the reaction is likely to be somewhat different. Not everyone can be part of the investigation team, but it is important to keep people informed of the progress being made by communicating as much information as possible to those who will be involved at the implementation stage.

Benchmarking is a tool for people who are serious about making improvements. Training is necessary, both at the awareness level and for practical application. The benchmarking process needs to be planned, steered, monitored and reviewed if maximum benefits are to accrue and the exercise is not to deteriorate into a 'nice to know' outcome. Trying to do too much too quickly will result in information overload and confused priorities; to allow people to become familiar with the methodology, two or three key areas for investigation are quite sufficient initially. Senior management support and recognition will then act as a spur for further activity.

What is to be benchmarked?

Benchmarking is not about making visits to other companies to 'try to pick up one or two ideas that may be useful somewhere'. Instead, it is centred around planned research which has been focused by a company's recognition that it needs to make improvements in critical business areas.

Improvement, generally, is initiated by asking

- Where do we want to be?
- Where are we now?
- What do we need to do to get from here to there?

Any activity that can be measured can be benchmarked, but most companies will start with those areas where they know they need to be competitive to remain in business. The company should have a clear mission statement or list of business goals which is used to focus improvement activity. Customer satisfaction is high on most company priority lists, as is the need for a low cost operation. Deciding these broad areas partly answers the question 'Where do we want to be?' These broad areas, however, need to be broken down into more specific activities that can be measured. What are the processes that deliver customer satisfaction? What processes eat up the costs? The more precisely you define what you need to measure, the more useful will be the information that you gather to compare it with.

What things are important to customers? What will help them to be successful? How good is the service currently given? What factors cause customer dissatisfaction? An analysis of customer complaints and warranty claims can give some guidance here and, of course, the customer can be asked directly. Questionnaires can be sent out and review workshops can be organised. 'Reliability' is a major requirement of most customers but what does it mean and how is it measured? Perhaps by on-time delivery performance or by levels of defect-free product. What key measures are already in place to monitor both current performance and the hoped-for improvement? What is your current performance in these areas and what is your current practice for achieving those performances?

The Cost of Quality approach for identifying areas for improvement has been dealt with fully in Chapter Four, but common areas for benchmarking are stock levels, work in progress, waste and reject levels. Again, the cost (measures) for each of these areas must be known but also it is essential to understand the processes and practices that lead to these costs being incurred. A thorough analysis of what actually happens is necessary, not a blind acceptance of a theoretical process model.

At the end of the day, you will need to understand how and why the companies you have benchmarked against have achieved their superiority, not just the levels of attainment that they have achieved. Comparing numbers will not help you to compete; it is necessary to compare the practices that have given rise to the numbers.

Emphasis has been placed on this initial step because, in the experience of leading benchmarking organisations like Xerox, it is here where most companies get it wrong. Until companies understand their processes fully and how those processes deliver the current performance in key areas, it is meaningless to make comparisons with other companies.

When the process is understood and the critical activities are known and measured, the 'Where are we now?' question has been answered. It should be clear where improvements could be made by investigating best practice elsewhere, i.e. the area to be benchmarked. It is essential to make sure, though, that the subjects chosen for benchmarking are based on current market demands and not just on areas that the company considers to be important. In the production of electronic components, for example, a defect-free supply is almost taken for granted; the requirements are for service differentiation and time to market.

Who to benchmark against?

Deciding on who to benchmark against depends on the subject chosen for benchmarking, the resources that can be made available, and the challenge that an organisation is prepared to undertake. In general, there are four different levels of benchmarking; each approach has its own advantages and disadvantages.

Internal benchmarking involves making comparisons with other parts of the same organisation. It can be with other departments, other sites, other companies within the same group, either in the same country or abroad. This type of benchmarking is usually straightforward to arrange and is fairly common. It is relatively easy to obtain all of the information necessary for a good comparison to be made. If the operations are similar across the different sites, the data will be instantly relevant and usable but it is unlikely to yield improvements which meet world best practice. Xerox, of course, started its journey by benchmarking internally and if this option is available to an organisation, it is an ideal first step.

Competitor benchmarking is much more difficult. Any information obtained is likely to be very relevant but, for reasons of confidentiality, it will be almost impossible to get a full picture of how a direct competitor operates. Looking at outputs and available figures can give some information but they can also mislead if the processes that deliver the outputs cannot be determined. Some of the larger organisations, however, do exchange information in selected areas in the interest of jointly coming to terms with best practice.

Functional benchmarking involves making comparisons with non-competitive organisations which carry out the same functional activity that you are interested in. Examples are warehousing, procurement, catering, etc. This type of benchmarking has several advantages: functional leaders are easy to identify in many areas; confidentiality is not usually an issue; approaches which may be novel for your industry can be discovered; two-way partnerships can be developed. Weighing against these, there are likely to be problems in adopting and adapting their practices for your operation.

Generic benchmarking goes a step further and may compare business processes which cut across various functions and in quite different industries. Opportunities discovered by this process are likely to be the most innovative and to create breakthroughs for unprecedented improvement. However, the integration of novel concepts into a different industry is also likely to be the most challenging.

The type of benchmarking and companies chosen to benchmark against depends on many factors. If your organisation is large and generally looked on as being a market leader, then the requirement is obviously different from that demanded by a smaller company with perhaps less experience of making quality improvements. The former will have a real need to search out best practices, whereas the latter will probably find it easy to identify improvement opportunities by observing the practices of almost any successful company.

Similarly, the level of resource that can be, and needs to be, committed in each case will be different. It makes sense to limit initial visits to local companies if possible; not only will the time and cost be less, but also problems associated with language and cultural differences will be avoided. Obviously, where the opportunity presents itself, internal benchmarking is the ideal place to start. Kodak do this between their sites, as do Philips. The whole process is relatively easy to manage and gives experience in the technique.

For other types of benchmarking, there are various sources of information which can aid in the identification of organisations to compare against. A simple starting point is the knowledge already within your own company; the marketing function, for example. Then, customers, suppliers and other contacts within the same industry can usually contribute good ideas. Consultants, academics and other industry observers can be asked who they think are the leaders in any particular area. Trade journals, magazines, books and other library material are useful and ideas can also be picked up at conferences, workshops and seminars.

One point should be mentioned. How do you know that the company which you have selected for benchmarking really represents best practice? The answer is that you don't – and perhaps never will. If the research you have carried out indicates that it is the best you have yet come across, and their performance is better than yours, then proceed to the next step. Perhaps somewhere there is someone a little better; you may discover them at a later date. It is important to halt the research, temporarily at least, and to start making improvements.

Some companies have sidestepped the issue of who to benchmark against by opting to use as a benchmark the requirements of the Malcolm Baldrige Quality Award. In Japan, companies have prepared themselves for the Deming Award in a similar way even though the requirements are less clearly defined and structured. The new European quality Award goes beyond Malcolm Baldrige in some areas and obviously it too presents an opportunity for making comparisons.

Collecting the benchmarking data

Although the most valuable information will be obtained by the direct exchange of data with other companies, much useful material can be gleaned from indirect sources. The sources mentioned in the previous section can be utilised, supplemented by information from annual reports, public databases, research institutes, government agencies, etc. Some of the data obtained by these means will be out of date and may be erroneous for other reasons.

Before descending upon other companies, it is vital to carry out as much desk research as possible in order to optimise the value of any visits. To supplement other sources, questionnaires can be prepared and sent to potential benchmark companies, for completion and return before the visit. Also, internal discussions should be held before the visits to establish the extent of current knowledge and to focus the requirements of the investigation so that a comprehensive checklist can be prepared.

Many companies who are not direct competitors are willing to allow access and share information, especially if it will be kept confidential. There will often be a need to sign a non–disclosure agreement. Personal contacts and a professional approach play a major part in opening doors; there is usually a need to convince target organisations that mutual benefit will accrue. Potential benchmarkers should be well briefed and be given sufficient authority to trade sensitive information. Often, a partnership for the exchange of data develops, with reciprocal visits and regular meetings to compare notes.

Independent bodies can be used to gather data from competitive companies but here it is often only the numbers that can be obtained and not the processes that deliver the numbers.

Analysing and using the data

The data from benchmarking exercises will obviously differ depending on the activity that has been investigated. However, it should be made up of two elements; what is achieved in terms of numbers (the performance metrics) and how and why it is achieved (the practice). Neither of these is of much use without the other. These two sets of data need to be considered and compared to your current performance in the same area. A further consideration may well be the difficulty of transferring a process that works well in one endeavour into a completely different industry.

The questions are:

- how big is the gap between your performance and theirs?

- how much of their experience is applicable to your situation?

If the data collected during the study is directly comparable, the performance gap is instantly meaningful. Even if your performance is superior there may be things to learn from what others do. The main lessons, though, come from studies which show that your performance is inferior. The question 'Where do we want to be?' can now be answered in detail, with quantified goals based on a knowledge of what the leaders are achieving and how. If the processes, products, company size or business areas are not very similar, then the interpretation of the data will be more difficult and the performance gap may not be as meaningful.

It may also be more difficult to answer 'How do we get from here to there?' What can be done to close the gap? How can the positions be reversed, bearing in mind that your competitors are also making improvements and trying to widen the gap? How far will you go to adopt and adapt new practices? What is involved, how much will it cost and how long will it take? What are the broader implications for the company? These are issues that need to be tackled on a team basis, involving those who really understand the current practices, those with responsibility for steering the future of the company and those with the authority to make the changes.

Once the decision is made to proceed, implementation of the changes must be planned and steered. New targets for the critical activity can be set based on the benchmark data, and good leadership will be essential to maintain focus and prevent backsliding. Progress towards the new objectives will need to be reviewed regularly and senior management have a key role to play in overseeing and providing support for the whole implementation process.

The next step
Successful companies have taken on board that improvement is a never-ending journey. A commitment to benchmarking as a driver for continuous improvement means that the implementation of a change to current practices is the end of the beginning, not the beginning of the end. Nothing stands still and as soon as a new

practice is established or a benchmark performance is reached, it may already be out of date. If the activity is still considered to be central to the organisation's existence, it is necessary constantly to review the benchmark for that activity and repeat the process of looking for best practice wherever it can be found. Xerox call this stage 'recalibrating the benchmark'.

7.3 Case study 1 – NCR (Manufacturing) Ltd

Background
When the National Cash Register Company of Dayton, Ohio, now known as NCR, set up in Dundee, they were the first multinational company to move to Scotland after the Second World War.

Operations began at the Camperdown factory in 1946 with the production of the 'Class 100' mechanical cash register which was manufactured there until 1972. In 1961 the company engaged in its first ever electronic production and within ten years, small electronic computer systems were in full production, leading the way for electronic point–of–sale terminals, banking terminals, document sorters, computer peripherals, accounting machines and general purpose computer systems.

The first engineering developments took place in 1957 with the design of two new cash registers which were manufactured until the 1970s. Electronic and System Integrated developments followed, creating a strong base for the company's engineering capabilities. NCR have always been ground-breaking in the use of new technologies for the design and manufacture of its products. Pioneers in the use of high density powder metallurgy, rubber to metal bonding, functional and decorative plastic mouldings and ergonomic design, in days when these were unheard of, NCR has always led the way.

Developments such as the encapsulation technique used successfully in No Carbon Required (NCR) paper, the Photo Chromic Micro Imaging (PCMI) process and adding to the Century family of computers ran along with the company's development programme of providing more efficient data capturing services. The evolution of Large Scale Integration (LSI) and Metal Oxide Semi-conductor (MOS) circuitry brought about a new range of data terminals for the retail, banking, commerce and industry markets.

The arrival of a new General Manager, James Adamson, coincided with the Research and Development team at the Gourdie factory designing the 1780 Automatic Teller Machine (ATM). In 1980, NCR Dundee was awarded a charter by the NCR Corporate Board in Dayton to design, develop and manufacture ATMs for the world market. NCR is now the market leader in this multi-million pound business, exporting to over 90 countries.

Below, we relate one example from NCR's experience with formal benchmarkaing which serves to illustrate the amount of research and effort that needs to be applied when selecting benchmarking partners.

Getting started

The task of getting the benchmarking process off the ground was taken on board by Ray S. Robertson, Manager, Operations Programme Management.

Prior to starting the benchmarking process itself, an initial step was to undertake a thorough research of all the available material on the subject. This established the diverse methods and approaches that could be used at the various stages of the process, the possible problems and pitfalls likely to be encountered and also a feel for the potential of the methodology for application within NCR.

Having established the ground rules, it was then appropriate to identify the subjects for benchmarking. NCR have a mission statement called 'Vision and Ten' which incorporates a declaration of purpose, a vision statement and the ten business goals that NCR has set itself. Guidance from this document was supplemented by asking all senior managers and directors what factors they thought were critical to the success of NCR. From these sources, the following list of 20 business measures (metrics) was arrived at:

- Concept to market

- Shipment performance
- Product reliability
- Order-to-ship cycle
- Manufacturing cycle time
- Production linearity
- Inventory (days on hand forward)
- Out-of-box quality
- Mainline yield
- On-time supplier delivery
- Supplier quality, mechanical/electrical
- Gross margin
- Return on assets
- Total value added per production employee
- Output per square foot
- Percent of parts on JIT
- Value of parts on JIT
- Revenue per employee
- Inventory accuracy
- Return on technical investment

A database was created to store information for each of these catergories.

Which companies to benchmark against?
It was decided to set a target of ten companies to benchmark against and, as a starting point, internal sources were consulted again. Approximately 90 managers and directors were interviewed and a list of 30 organisations was drawn up. A standard letter was sent to the Managing Director or Chief Executive of all of these companies, enquiring whether they would be interested in a joint benchmarking exercise with NCR, involving the sharing of performance data and best practices. Only 13 replies were received and out of these five were negative, one because of over-commitment to other benchmarking exercises. Furthermore, because two of the companies approached are part of the same organisation, this meant that the list of possible benchmarking partners was down to seven

from the original list of 30.

The next step was to send to the seven remaining companies, a list of the benchmarking metrics that NCR was interested in pursuing and to establish the performance levels currently being achieved by those companies for each of the metrics. Only one questionnaire was fully completed but it was felt that sufficient information had been obtained to indicate that visits to all of the companies would be worthwhile. However, to keep the costs and the time involved within acceptable limits, only four companies were selected for visiting at this stage. One of the four visits, though, showed that first impressions are not always reliable.

Of the three companies not visited as part of this exercise, one had been visited previously on other exercises and demonstrated world-class manufacturing techniques. The second was very receptive to the idea of a visit but the timing of the enquiry was inconvenient for specific reasons. The third company made a visit to NCR, a good relationship was established and an invitation was made for a reciprocal visit.

However, it was not felt that sufficient useful benchmarking data could be obtained solely by pursuing the contacts already made and it was decided to cast the net wider.

Identifying the best companies in the world

A literature search was carried out to identify the optimum source for a list of the best companies in the world. Many published lists were uncovered and investigated including the *Times 1000*, the *Electronic Business 200*, *Japan's Top 50 Companies Turn in a Strong Performance* and *Fortune 500*. From these, the latter was chosen since it gives a large list of companies around the world and is not focused on any specific area of endeavour. It lists the world's largest industrial corporations in terms of sales, profits, assets, stockholders' equity and employees. Within *Fortune 500*, companies are classified into 27 industrial groupings and it was decided to select those eight groupings with either technology or product similar to NCR. This gave a total list of 155 companies broken down into the following areas:

Aerospace	16
Computers (including office equipment)	15
Electronics	45
Industrial and farm equipment	28
Motor vehicles and parts	40
Scientific and photographic equipment	7
Toys, sporting goods	1
Transportation equipment	3
Total:	155

The aim has been to analyse and compare the performances of about 100 companies and to select suitable benchmarking partners from the comparisons made. However, the decision was made to follow up on all 155 organisations; the question was 'How?' The previous activity had already consumed a considerable amount of time and money, the initial response had been poor and the exercise had, to date, yielded insufficient usable material.

For this stage of the investigation, it was decided that a well-designed questionnaire would provide the maximum amount of necessary information, quickly, and at minimum cost. Considerable research, thought and effort was put into designing a suitable questionnaire and a pilot run was carried out on some of the contacts established in the earlier exercise. One of the aims of the design was brevity – so that people would not be discouraged from filling it in. With this in mind, it was decided to reduce the number of metrics being researched. This was achieved by inviting the directors and managers within NCR to revise and prioritise their previous selections. The list was reduced from 20 to the following 13.

- Mainline yield (right-first-time production)
- Product reliability (mean time between failures – in hours)
- Out–of–box quality (simulates customer's perception of quality)
- Concept–to–market (also called 'time to market', measured in weeks)
- Research and development costs versus plan

- Development schedule versus plan
- Inventory (days of material on hand)
- Manufacturing cycle time (a measure equatable to responsiveness)
- Revenue growth (to indicate trends)
- Return on assets
- Return on revenue
- Revenue per employee
- Revenue per production employee

This list of categories, and definitions for each, formed the meat of the questionnaire, with the potential respondent being asked to enter his/her company's performance data in the space provided beside each metric. Further questions were included to establish the size and type of business, the company's experience of benchmarking and interest in benchmarking with NCR, and the respondent's name and position. Considerable space was given to explaining the purpose of the questionnaire, assuring the recipient of NCR's commitment to maintain confidentiality and a promise that all who responded would receive a summary of the findings of the survey. In all, the questionnaire consisted of five uncrowded A4 pages.

Locating the address and person to contact for each company proved to be a greater obstacle than had been anticipated. Since most company directories are country-specific, the list of companies had to be classified by country and then the appropriate directory consulted. Only 138 of the original 155 companies were eventually located and the questionnaire was sent out with an explanatory letter to the top person within each organisation.

The response was again disappointing, with 111 companies (80 per cent) not responding at all. Of the other 27, four declined to participate for sensitivity reasons, 12 declined because of other commitments and four returned only their annual reports. Only seven companies (5 per cent) responded fully. Research had indicated that between 9 per cent and 15 per cent could have been expected. Perhaps the approach had been made at the wrong level; perhaps the metrics requested were not pursued by some companies; perhaps there were language problems in some cases since many of the organisations were in countries where English is not the first language.

Analysis

Data from each company were letter-coded to ensure confidentiality and performances were indexed, with the best company (the benchmark) scoring 100. The indexed values for each company were drawn on to bar graphs for a visual display of the different performance levels within each metric.

No one company did best in all of the metrics and there was a tie for one category:

Companies A and J came out top for one metric each;

Company B was the best for two metrics;

Companies C and E were top in three metrics;

NCR came top in four of the metrics.

Companies D, F, G, H, I and K did not come top in any of the metrics.

Since all of the organisations used for the comparison are major companies, it is clear that it is not essential to be number one in every area in order to be successful. Perhaps not surprisingly, all of the companies did well in the out-of-box quality category with there being very little difference between the best and the worst. In other areas, the differences were more marked, sometimes dramatically so. Although the amount of information collected was less than hoped for, it was sufficient for comparisons to be made and to indicate how NCR were placed in the key areas selected.

NCR achieved a benchmark performance in four of the 13 key areas that were selected as being critical to its success. However, they are determined not to get complacent. The comparisons recorded above are quantitative and were made purely by comparing the available numbers. They do not take into account the different industries, the product being made, the processes and the conditions that led to the numbers being generated. (Some of the financial measures, though, are certainly a good guide to the health of any company).

NCR, of course, have more detail about each of the companies who took part in the study and have made a more detailed qualitative comparison. They are committed to carrying out follow-up investigations into those critical areas where they feel there is room for further improvement. Based on the findings of the study and other data collected, they have identified the companies worth pursuing as benchmarking partners and have carried out more desk research to discover as much as possible about the companies selected before arranging further visits.

CASE STUDY 2 – XEROX

Background

Benchmarking is a key element in Xerox's business strategy. At the highest level in the business, ten critical parameters have been defined; at the next level, a further 13 have been identified; each of these 23 critical success factors has a benchmark performance against it – what Xerox consider to be the best of the best, and these are continuously updated.

Every aspect of Xerox's business is benchmarked and some of their reported successes in diverse areas are:

- Incoming parts acceptance improved to 99.5 per cent
- Inventory reduced by two-thirds
- Engineering drawings per man doubled
- Marketing productivity improved by one-third
- Service labour cost reduced by 30 per cent
- Distribution productivity increased by 8–10 per cent

Xerox's first benchmarking experience was mentioned earlier in the chapter. The next major exercise, and the one that is used as an example in Camp's book, involved L.L. Bean, an American mail-order company and retailer of outdoor clothing. For their warehousing/distribution operation, Xerox identified L.L. Bean as the functional leader to benchmark against because of its superiority in the areas of order-picking and warehousing. Even though the business area is completely different, the basic operation carried out by the function is very similar.

The benchmarking process

Xerox have a clearly-defined ten step process for benchmarking:

1. Identify benchmarking subject
2. Identify comparative companies
3. Determine data collection method and collect data
4. Determine current competitive gap
5. Project future performance
6. Communicate findings and gain acceptance
7. Establish functional goals
8. Develop action plans
9. Implement plans and monitor progress
10. Recalibrate benchmark.

In their experience, the area where most people go wrong is at step one. Even within Xerox, there are still people who make site visits and consider that they are carrying out a benchmarking exercise. However, unless the good ideas observed during a visit are in line with the improvement priorities established back at base, there will be little chance of getting them implemented. Without a clear definition of what it is that needs changing, without prioritised goals for improvement, any visits are unfocused.

Improvement opportunities are identified by recognising the critical processes which deliver the critical success factors in the market place. The critical processes are then analysed and the improvement opportunities identified are prioritised. For example, Xerox have three business objectives as a corporation:

- Customer satisfaction
- Employee satisfaction
- Return on assets

For return of assets, a cause and effect diagram has been used to analyse and give greater understanding of the contributory factors and how attention should be prioritised for benchmarking activity. Within their Marketing Group, ten areas were identified:

- Customer Marketing
- Customer Engagement
- Order Fulfilment
- Product Maintenance
- Billing and Collection
- Financial Management
- Asset Management
- Business Management
- Information Technology
- Human Resource Management

Within these ten areas, 67 sub-processes were identified. Each of these sub-processes became candidates for the improvement process.

Selecting companies to benchmark against
To get information on suitable benchmarking companies, Xerox subscribe to ABI Information, an American management database. They also have access to a large technical database. When searching for someone to benchmark against for their warehousing/ distribution operation in 1981, they collected and analysed material from 11 organisations. Databases were consulted, magazines and trade journals covering a three-year period were reviewed, professional associations were asked and consulting firms were contacted.

Although benchmarking is carried out internally and against direct competitors, it is by carrying out functional and generic benchmarking that Xerox have identified their greatest improvement opportunities. Xerox used American Express as their benchmark for invoicing processes, Florida Power and Light for their quality management processes and Ford and Cummins Engines for their factory layout.

Currently, for supplier development, Honda Manufacturing of America are being benchmarked. At the time of the study, Xerox had ten engineers working with suppliers to improve quality. Honda, meanwhile, a comparative company in terms of costs, have a dedicated supplier development team of 96, over half of whom are graduate engineers! And this for a key supplier base of 216 for assembled parts, which is somewhat less than Xerox's list of suppliers.

According to Roger Sugden of Rank Xerox Ltd, the following points are key for successful benchmarking:

- It is essential to understand your own processes thoroughly.
- Visits are not arranged until sufficient desk research has been carried out to ensure that the companies selected are the best that can be found.
- The focus must be on Industry Best Practices.
- There must be a willingness to share information. Reciprocal visits are arranged if required.
- Sensitive information is always kept confidential.
- Getting the process owners or operators to carry out the benchmarking studies is seen as being critical; trying to involve people after the study is too late.
- Don't concentrate on outcomes; it is the practices and processes that need to be understood.
- Benchmarking must be a continuous process; the competition is constantly changing.
- There must be a willingness to change based on the benchmark findings.

8. Beyond Measurement? – Customer Perception and Quality Function Deployment

Customer perception and customer behaviour is, of course, a major area of importance for a book on quality. It is not, however, of major importance on its own account in this particular book on Quality Measuring and Monitoring. Rather, the measurement of customer perception and the connection between customers' perception and the internal measurement of businesses processes within the organisation, are what concern us here. How do we tie what our customers, and potentially other stakeholders, think about the necessary and desired features of products and services, to quality delivering and quality improvement activities within the business? How do we focus the business on what the customer wants, on the **Voice of the Customer?**

There are a myriad views on customer perception. For example, Tom Peters tells us that perception is never neutral, it is either positive or negative. He tells us that customer perception is the sum of lots of little things and that a bad impression is ten times more powerful than a good impression. He also tells us that in product design, we need lots of features which are different small hooks for different folks, and that the chance of hooking the customer is proportional to the number of hooks. **Above all, he tells us that perception is all there is.**

Japanese companies constantly measure and monitor customer satisfaction and perception as part of the heart of their corporate strategy. They concentrate on customer service, product reliability, quality, guarantees and improving customer relations. Numerous methods of monitoring customer service and quality are used. For example,

1. Regular meeting between customers and senior management;
2. Detailed market research on existing customers' needs and expectations, as well as those of potential customers;
3. Surveys and questionnaires yielding information from internal and external customers regarding potential improvements to both products and services;
4. Customer clinics and quality service forums which allow the company to listen and act as appropriate to improve service and achieve service excellence;
5. Comment cards delivered with the service or attached to products, which the customer is encouraged to complete, and which when returned are always seen and acted upon by senior management;
6. A comprehensive analysis of all customer complaints as opportunities for improvement;
7. Support help lines and free telephone numbers.

Juran sees measurement as the way out of the customer perception problems. Because words have multiple meanings to different people, misunderstandings can arise in the translation of customer needs into the language that is used inside the business, that exists to satisfy those needs.

Through this diversity of approaches to the perception of customers, it becomes clear that we need to take such customer perception into account in developing products and services, delivering them and monitoring their relevance to the customer's requirements. Secondly, we need a unified approach to doing this, which does not result in consequential information loss due to human interpretation at various points through the process of deployment. Thirdly, we need to ensure completeness in that all aspects of customer perception have been included and that the model we are building is coherent and not inherently self contradictory. Fourthly, we need to avoid the frequent changes, the lack of clarity, the lack of clear authority and responsibility, and the cycling and recycling, associated with our traditional approaches to product development. To some extent, these problems occur also in service provision.

An approach developed in Japan in the 1970s provides us with a solution to these needs. The technique of Quality Function Deployment (QFD) is about translating the Voice of the Customer into design features or internal business processes. It helps us to concentrate on what matters to the customer and not on what we, in our own language inside the business, think matters. The idea of the Voice of the Customer can be extended, also, to voices of other stakeholders.

8.2 QUALITY FUNCTION DEPLOYMENT AND THE VOICE OF THE CUSTOMER

QFD originates from Mitsubishi Heavy Industries in the early 1970s, and was taken up by Toyota Autobody in the late 1970s. QFD is best thought of as an approach rather than a technique, since, like other Japanese methodologies it relies heavily on teamwork, and much of the benefit comes out of clear, concise team planning and communication. Along with Taguchi methodology (see Chapter 10), Quality Function Deployment is taken as one of the two major tools of Simultaneous or Concurrent Engineering.

QFD is a planning technique to ensure that design of both products and processes are customer-focused. It uses a series of matrices – Houses of Quality – to link customer needs with product or process features. On each matrix, customer needs are represented by rows, and product or process features or 'hows' are represented by columns. The body of the matrix gives the strength of relationships between needs and the way they will be, or are being, met. The roof of the house gives the correlation between the hows, and the right-hand wing of the house gives a benchmark of performance in satisfying the needs against major competitors or possibly best practice. These aspects of the Houses of Quality tend to be fairly standard, but other aspects tend to vary between applications. A basic House of Quality is illustrated in Figure 8.1. The bullseye symbol is used to represent a strong relationship, a circle a medium relationship and a triangle a weak relationship. Sometimes these are reserved for positive relationships only, with different symbols for the equivalent negative ones.

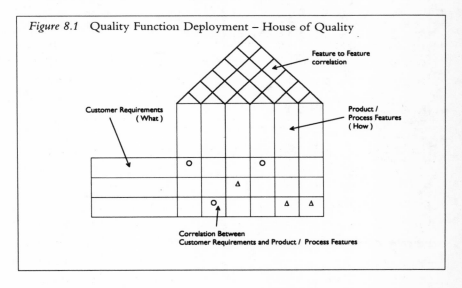

Figure 8.1   Quality Function Deployment – House of Quality

A further example is shown in Figure 8.2. This represents a House of Quality for a retail laundry. From the House we see that a survey of customers has revealed that what matters to the customers are that the clothes are Completely Clean, that there is Perfect Press, that the Correct Clothes are returned and the Correct Service provided and that there is a Quick Turn Around and a Friendly Service. The customer survey also revealed that what was of most importance to the customer was not that the clothes were completely clean, but instead that the correct clothes were returned and the correct service given. Accordingly, in the table this is represented by a weighting of five. The second most important aspect was viewed

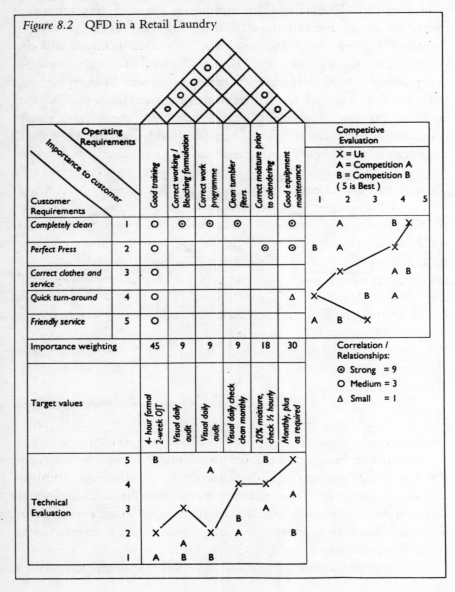

Figure 8.2   QFD in a Retail Laundry

by the customer as a Friendly Service (four), then Quick Turn Around (three), then Perfect Press (two), then Completely Clean (one).

The retail laundry sees its achievement of these five customer requirements to be obtained through the six operating requirements identified as columns of the House of Quality. These are Good Training, Correct Washing/Bleaching Formulation, Correct Wash Programme, Clean Tumbler Filters, Correct Moisture Prior to Calendering and Good Equipment Maintenance. Looking at the body of the table, we see that the most important aspect to the customer, Correct Clothes and Correct Service, only has a single (medium) relationship to one of the operating requirements – Good Training. This is also true for the second most important aspect to the customer – Friendly Service. The next most important aspect to the customer – a Quick Turn Around – also has a weak dependence on Good Equipment Maintenance. Interestingly enough, it is only the two least important customer requirements out of the five that we have identified, which are well supported by the operating requirements inside the organisation; Perfect Press has a strong relationship with Correct Moisture Prior to Calendering and Good Equipment Maintenance, as well as its medium relationship with Good Training. Completely Clean Clothes depends strongly on the Correct Washing/Bleaching Formulation, the Correct Wash Programme, the Cleanness of the Tumbler Filters and Good Equipment Maintenance as well as having a medium relationship with Good Training.

In the roof of the House of Quality we see the relationships between the various operating requirements that satisfy the customer requirements. Good Training has medium relationships with the provision of the Correct Wash/Bleach Formulation, the provision of the Correct Wash Programme, the provision of Clean Tumbler Filters and the provision of Correct Moisture Prior to Calendering. Good Equipment Maintenance has medium relationships with Clean Tumbler Filters and Correct Moisture Prior to Calendering. Other relationships, of course, may exist in reality.

The importance of the various operating requirements may be

calculated from the importance of the customer requirements and the weightings given by the correlations in the body of the table. As an illustration, consider Friendly Service – this has a customer importance weighting of four and is connected to Good Training by a medium relationship which has a weighting of three. Friendly Service, then, contributes four times three, which equals twelve, to the importance weighting of Good Training. Proceeding in a similar way with each of the other four customer requirements, and in each case multiplying by three (because of the medium relationships with Good Training) and then adding up each of the contributions, we come to a total importance weighting of 45 for Good Training. For each of the other measures, proceeding similarly, we obtain the importance weightings shown in the table.

From these weightings it is clear that Good Training is the most important operating requirement, not because any customer requirement depends strongly on it, but because all customer requirements are related to it, albeit only by medium relationships. The next most important operating requirement is Good Equipment Maintenance, followed some way back by Correct Moisture Prior to Calendering. The three remaining operating requirements are of equal importance. These weightings will help to prioritise effort in terms of meeting the customer requirement. Clearly here, most effort must be given to ensuring and maintaining Good Training and Good Equipment Maintenance.

If we now consider the right-hand wing of the House of Quality, this contains information which **benchmarks** our performance as a retail laundry against that of our main competitors. For example, for Completely Clean Clothes we can see that our customers have given us a rating of four, on a five point scale on which five is best, against a rating of three and a half for our competitor B, and of two for our competitor A. We are clearly doing better. This is also true in terms of Perfect Press, where we are well ahead of both our competitors. We are also ahead on Friendly Service. However, we are behind on Correct Clothes and Service, and Quick Turn Around. This is particularly important for Correct Clothes and Service, because this is regarded as most important by our customers. This benchmarking enables us to see that we must improve on Correct Clothes and Service and Quick Turn Around to have a competitive edge over our competitors.

The basement of the House of Quality contains the calculated importance weightings and also target values and technical evaluations. The target values represent the targets on the operating requirements. The technical evaluation represents benchmarking our operating requirements against those of our competitors.

In product development applications of Quality Function Deployment, a single House of Quality would be not used, but several, as is illustrated in Figure 8.3. The first house (Product Planning) would translate customer wants into design requirements. These then form the input to the second house (Part Deployment) where design requirements are mapped to part characteristics. In the third house (Process Planning) part characteristics are mapped to key process operations, and in the fourth house (Production Planning) key process operations are mapped to production requirements. Other houses may be introduced as needed, for example for installation, if appropriate.

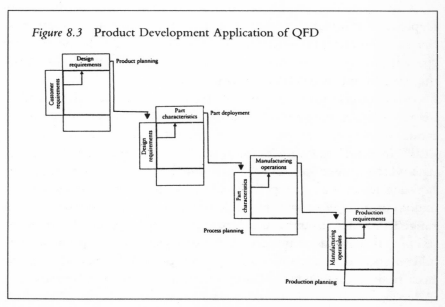

Figure 8.3 Product Development Application of QFD

Applied correctly, Quality Function Deployment should make use of an interfunctional team composed of representatives of all those involved in, or with interests in, the development of the product, or service, from market research through design, development, manufacturing and delivery to the customer. Small teams are preferable, of six to eight individuals of equal status. Specialists may be co-opted as needed. Open minds are needed, as well as experience.

Attendance at the series of team meetings should be a high priority. On major projects, perhaps as many as sixty hours or more of meetings may be required. These need to be in the project plan. Teams need training, and consensus, rather than voting, should be the order of operation amongst the personnel from production planning, research, design and development, marketing, product engineering, manufacturing, purchasing, service, installation, quality and tooling who may be involved.

First projects need careful implementation. Teams should be chosen carefully, as should be the project, and both should be monitored to ensure that things do not go wrong.

One possible set of steps for applying Quality Function Deployment (in development) is shown in Figure 8.4. It is apparent that no high technology is needed to use the approach, although specialist software has been marketed in this area. Little training in the technique is required, although training and mentoring is necessary to change the work pattern, to establish discipline and to help to remove the functional barriers. Also, little specialist skill is required since the complexity which might at first sight be apparent in the method, really arises because we are no longer overlooking data which is overlooked in the conventional approach. There is also no knowledge loss, or repetition of work, with the QFD approach, and accordingly time and resource reductions claimed can be in the range from a half to one third. However, it must be stated that this is in companies who are mature in the use of QFD. First projects may add to normal development times. The use of QFD should include both basic and excitement features – in the case of the laundry, for instance, the basic cleaning process was not the most important aspect to the customer – he took this for granted. Similarly with an automobile, it is the aesthetic design features, not the basic functionality, which is often most attractive to a customer.

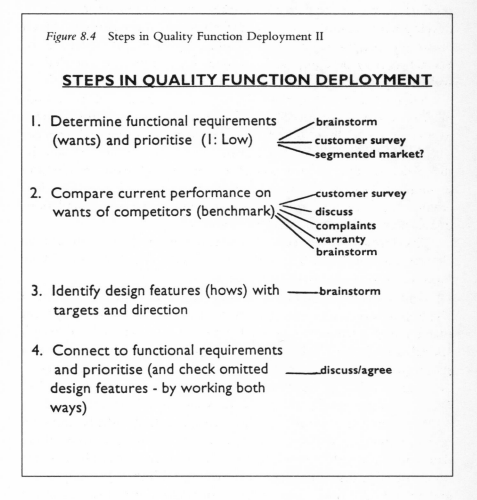

Figure 8.4 Steps in Quality Function Deployment II

STEPS IN QUALITY FUNCTION DEPLOYMENT

1. Determine functional requirements
    (wants) and prioritise (1: Low) — brainstorm — customer survey — segmented market?

2. Compare current performance on
    wants of competitors (benchmark) — customer survey — discuss — complaints — warranty — brainstorm

3. Identify design features (hows) with —— brainstorm
    targets and direction

4. Connect to functional requirements
    and prioritise (and check omitted —— discuss/agree
    design features - by working both
    ways)

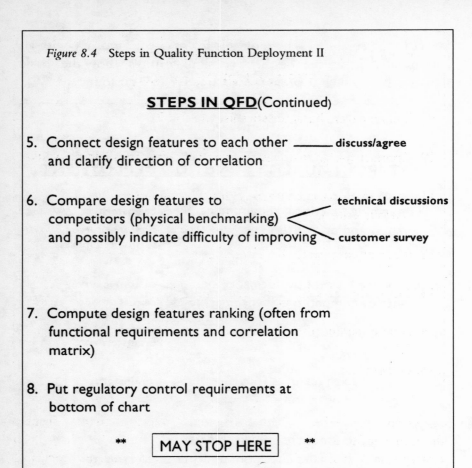

Figure 8.4 Steps in Quality Function Deployment II

STEPS IN QFD(Continued)

5. Connect design features to each other ———— discuss/agree
   and clarify direction of correlation

6. Compare design features to   technical discussions
   competitors (physical benchmarking)
   and possibly indicate difficulty of improving customer survey

7. Compute design features ranking (often from
   functional requirements and correlation
   matrix)

8. Put regulatory control requirements at
   bottom of chart

   **   MAY STOP HERE   **

Figure 8.4   Steps in Quality Function Deployment III

STEPS IN QFD(Continued)

9. Define parts characteristics list (matrix 2)

10. Connect design features to parts characteristics and prioritise

11. Benchmark parts characteristics to competitors
    (various criteria - how good, cost)

12. Interconnect parts characteristics

13. Compute parts characteristics ranking

14. Define manufacturing operations

15. etc, etc, etc.

Used properly, Quality Function Deployment ensures discipline, structure and conformance to time scales which have been clearly stated. It also ensures a team attitude and breaches functional boundaries. It ensures recognition of customer satisfaction and the anticipation and prioritisation of customer needs. As a consequence of its use the customer only gets, and only pays for, what he requires, and it helps in the development of a whole life-cycle attitude. QFD presents a continuous thread of information and communication throughout the organisation. All aspects of quality of customer service are covered. It helps ensure attention to detail and detailed pre-planning. As a consequence of its use, actions and resources are also moved upstream, informed decisions are made, and complex interactions clarified. By QFD we achieve problem avoidance which gives us competitive advantage. Some benefits of QFD are shown in Figure 8.5.

Figure 8.5   Some Benefits of QFD

Improved quality

Improved product reliability

Reduced warranty claims

Lower cost in design and manufacture

Opportunity for improved profitability and improved company performance

Reduced decision/planning time and improved decision making

Improved productivity of technical and other staff

A more customer-orientated workforce

Better reaction to marketing opportunities

To achieve these advantages and benefits, however, QFD must

- be team-based
- have coherence
- have access to full market information
- be documented at each stage
- be reviewed and agreed at the next meeting
- be based on individuals bringing information into the meetings and doing work between meetings
- be team-based not committee-based
- be disciplined
- focus on voice of customer
- have top level commitment
- be open to the customer, and
- be viewed as a process, not as a technique.

The difficulties that tend to arise in the application of Quality Function Deployment are in themselves really advantages, since they force the clarification of issues which are often only implicit in the conventional approach. Thus, they force the resolution of these issues and the consistency of the development programme. Some such difficulties are shown in Figure 8.6.

Figure 8.6 Difficulties → advantages in clarification

1. Ignorant customers – especially on needs
2. Too late decisions or authorisation to proceed
3. Lack of clarity in responsibility/authorisation to define
4. Changes (iterations), e.g. in design features
   by others/management
   late
   in conflict with design philosophy or parts
   procurement policy, etc.
5. Non standard features/orders
6. Lack of attention to detail
7. First project and team

Quality Function Deployment has a good record of use in Japan, the US and increasingly Europe. Companies such as Rank Xerox, Ford and DEC have achieved, in some cases, staggering results from the use of QFD techniques, However, automotive applications are still probably amongst the most common.

Quality Function Deployment techniques are often introduced as part of Simultaneous Engineering or Concurrent Engineering. In the Simultaneous Engineering approach, a multi–disciplinary taskforce is used as management, at a higher level, to ensure that there is simultaneous development of product, manufacturing equipment and processes, quality control and marketing. The product is defined in customer terms and translated into engineering terms by QFD.

Also, however, products and processes are optimised, and design for manufacture and assembly is applied. Applications of Simultaneous Engineering can be seen in Honda, Mazda and Nissan in the 1970s and 80s; and Chrysler, Ford, General Motors, Xerox, Digital by the mid 1980s. In Europe, there are now numerous applications including Volkswagen, Daimler Benz, Opal and Fiat. Simultaneous Engineering is the way round the backtracking and cycling prevalent in development processes, the escalating costs, late delivery or poor quality because the product is hard to make. Like QFD, it deals with whether the customer really wants the product and the interdepartmental fences, suspicion, fights and blame that take place within our organisation. It is also a counter to the barriers to information flow, to functional isolation, and to the lack of application of focusing tools and a comprehensive disciplined approach with clarity and purpose. Above all, it ensures early involvement of suppliers and departments. The result is accelerated time to market, lower cost and less hassle.

8.3 FROM QFD TO THE TABLE OF TABLES

Various versions of QFD and extensions to QFD have been developed. Numerous forms of Houses of Quality are in use within certain organisations, such as Motorola. A particularly interesting example of the extension of Quality Function Deployment, is that developed by Florida Power and Light (first international prize winners of The Deming Prize), known as the Table of Tables. This is a matrix that cross-relates customer requirements and specific quality elements in internal administration, but which also pulls together all the different major customer groups within a single table.

Florida Power and Light (FPL) see a number of steps in their process of generating a Table of Tables. Firstly, they decide who the customers are; that is, they identify the major customer groups by de-aggregating the total market and services provided. The second step is to survey the customers to obtain data on needs. These are then weighted for importance and grouped into 19 quality elements. These elements include courteous customer service, continuity of service, environmental protection and so on.

The fourth stage is to begin to determine the relationship between the Voice of the Customer and FPL internal activities. To do this different customer groups are weighted, based on their size and usage of electricity. The fifth stage is to apply this weighting, ranked in importance with the 19 quality elements. In doing this, direct and indirect quality elements are combined; indirect elements correspond to those for organisations that represent and speak to the customer, such as a nuclear regulatory commission and the Florida Public Service Commission. Carrying on through this process they arrive at the overall ranking of the quality elements.

The next step is to prioritise FPL activities based on what quality elements the customer identified as the most important. This stage being complete, it is then summarised on to one large sheet of paper – the Table of Tables.

The FPL approach to the Table of Tables has been developed and fine-tuned over a considerable number of years. However, the approach of the Table of Tables does not have to be complicated. Florida Power and Light use the Table of Tables to communicate the Voice of the Customer to all its employees. It is sent to every work location with instructions that it be set on the wall next to the bulletin boards, and in this way every employee can see what the customer thinks is important. FPL has repeated this process on an annual basis.

An illustration of the approach of the Table of Tables is shown in Figure 8.7. Individual Houses of Quality for the different customer groups are weighted and combined to form a single Table of Tables, whilst still retaining the visual impact of the individual customer groups and what matters to them. We can also see what matters to the aggregate and how the individual Tables or Houses contribute.

This approach could, of course, be extended to other stakeholders as well as just customer groups, so that a Table of Tables might combine the interests of various stakeholders. This, however, would be more complex and is currently the subject of development activity for the team at Nottingham.

Figure 8.7 Table of Tables

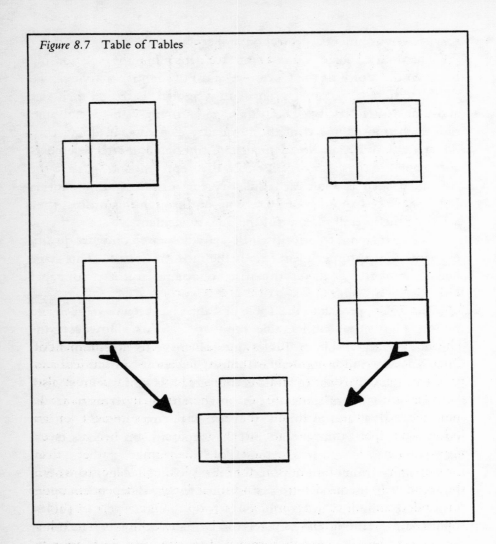

9. How Do You Measure Up? – The Measurement of Personal Quality

9.1 BACKGROUND TO PERSONAL QUALITY

This book examines and discusses approaches to the Measurement of Quality, that is, measurement within organisations, of services and products, of departments and processes. However, we must also consider how we might measure our own individual performance as managers. By this is meant the personal measurement of an individual's performance, in order for him or her to seek improvement in their method of managing, rather than measurement by another person, for example the manager to whom they report. Any consideration of personal quality is dependent upon our understanding of what motivates people. One aspect of this is top management attitudes as perceived by the workforce. The other area where there is a clear importance of measurement in relation to people themselves is in their role as employees rather than as customers, which was dealt with in the preceding chapter on customer perception and Quality Function Deployment. Measuring oneself can be the driving force for personal quality improvement in our own work and life. This can form the basis, or part of the basis for organisation improvement and fits naturally into modern concepts of TQM.

If Total Quality Management is to succeed, then it must be seen to be taken seriously at the top of the organisation. It is only when the Chief Executive or senior management are convinced of the value of Total Quality Management that effective and lasting changes will take place.

Encouraging people within the organisation to become involved with the Total Quality Management initiative is crucial. It is, therefore, essential that we have some understanding of the individuals at work, and their motives.

Abraham Maslow (1908–1970) postulated a 'hierarchy of needs' for individuals. This theory assumes that, once a need is satisfied, the individual strives to achieve the next higher need. If a man's appetite for food is satisfied, he is no longer motivated by hunger. When he feels safe and secure he seeks out love, and so on up hierarchy to the need for fulfilment of ambitions and self-realisation. This is illustrated in Figure 9.1

Figure 9.1 Hierarchy of needs

Achievement, ambition

Esteem, self respect status

Belonging, friendship

Safety, protection

Physiological needs

Some conclusions suggest themselves when we consider this hierarchy; for example, that it is pointless to try to motivate by offering friendship if there is an unfulfilled need for sleep. If a need is unsatisfied at a lower level, then according to Maslow higher needs have little influence.

The basic principle of Maslow's theory is that once a need has been satisfied it ceases to act as a motivator. There is some doubt as to whether a satisfied need ceases entirely to motivate or whether it just ceases to be a prime motivator, but for practical purposes a satisfied lower need is treated as non-motivating as far as developing higher motivation goes. It may be said that a person is still interested in his safety, for example, although he is safe and secure, but this is unlikely to lead to much action unless safety is actively threatened.

Frederick Herzberg (b.1923) studied the factors mentioned by employees in connection with events at work about which they felt particularly satisfied or dissatisfied.

Satisfying (Motivators)	Dissatisfying (Hygiene Factors)
Achievement	Company policy and admin.
Recognition	Interpersonal relationships
Responsibility	Working conditions
Advancement	Supervision
The work itself	Status
Growth potential	Impact on home
Wages	Wages

Herzberg's concept was that the removal of dissatisfying (hygiene) factors does not lead to *positive* motivation, but merely removes barriers to real satisfaction and motivation. One can draw an analogy here. If we ensure that our homes are clean, and that debris and rubbish are cleared away, this will not, of itself, make us healthy. It merely prevents us from becoming unhealthy. Likewise, removal of a 'dissatisfaction' factor will not motivate, but will prevent and avoid demotivation.

It is important to put these theories into context, otherwise there is a danger of over-simplification. Both of them are based on work done in the early 1950s, in the United States, and chiefly on male workers. Society, and people's attitudes to work, have changed since then. The educational system, the changes in moral standards, declining influence of the home, relative affluence, have all led to new attitudes to work. Some of these attitudes may be difficult for more conventional managers to accept. But some attitudes, especially towards menial and repetitive work, and higher aspirations, can help managers achieve the changes they seek to make.

9.2 GROUP BEHAVIOUR

The above theories are about individual behaviour. But there is plenty of practical evidence that personal behaviour is substantially influenced when the employee is part of a group or team. The behaviour of a group is not the same as that of the sum of the individuals who make up that group. A group of people who work together regularly and whose performance in part depends on each other's efforts quickly develops its own attitudes to authority, its own rules of behaviour and working practices. It supports its own individual members and its members draw strength from each other. It also forces its members into well defined roles from which the individual can escape only with great difficulty.

Since people draw both security and status from groups it is not surprising that changes which threaten their position will be perceived as a personal threat, and may be strongly resisted by the group as well as by individuals. And it does not matter whether the threat is real; it is how it is perceived that matters.

9.3 PERSONAL QUALITY

Total Quality Management aims to give people, both as individuals and teams, real responsibility for their work, and for improvement. This book is concerned with the importance of measuring and monitoring quality; one aspect of this is the monitoring and measurement of our own personal quality performance.

Claus Møller, the Danish business economist and founder of Time Manager International, has focused on individual and personal quality as the basis for all other types of quality. His experiences of businesses made Møller convinced that administrative processes, rather than production processes, offered more opportunities for overall improvements in performance.

In order to improve service to the customer, Møller believes that the people who actually produce the goods must be inspired to achieve the best possible performance, and that a major cultural adjustment is required by everyone. Møller believes this will only be achieved by improving personal development of the individual. This, he believes, will lead to increased competence and performance in the three key areas of Productivity, Relations and Quality. TMI sees these three areas as 'evergreens', not fads, but intrinsic to all people's lives and so closely interwoven that they presuppose each other.

Møller focuses on the measurement of personal quality as the basis for quality improvement. He has identified two standards of personal quality: the ideal performance level (IP) and the actual performance level (AP).

The ideal performance level is each individual's personal quality goal, and is a value much influenced by experiences in the formative years. Hence, the IP level will fluctuate in the early period of the individual's life and stabilise as adulthood is reached, and will be influenced only by strong emotional experiences. The IP level has a decisive effect on each individual's development and future potential.

Actual performance (AP) level is influenced by the individual's self-esteem, that is, how the person feels about him or herself. The AP level is influenced by the acknowledgement of others regarding performance, understanding the goals and why a specific task has to be performed. Other factors can influence the AP level – success or failure, the environment, experience and skills, the nature of the task, the time available, other people's AP levels, and the IP level of the individual himself. Møller has twelve **Golden Rules** to help improve the AP level. They are:

1. Set personal quality goals.
2. Establish your own personal quality account.
3. Check how satisfied others are with your efforts.
4. Regard the next link as a valued customer.
5. Avoid errors.
6. Perform tasks more effectively.

7. Utilise resources well.
8. Be committed.
9. Learn to finish what you start – strengthen your self-discipline.
10. Control your stress.
11. Be ethical – maintain your integrity.
12. Demand quality.

Møller has also developed two simple techniques for raising personal quality:

- The 'do/check' system (continuous self-checking the quality of performance).
- The quality business card. (Devise a card which is a personal guarantee of quality of work).

Møller has recommended ways of raising the IP level of young people, and discusses the links of personal quality to departmental, product, service and company quality. He has developed simple exercises which can be utilised for the evaluation and improvement of, for example, actual individual performance level, checking how satisfied others are with our efforts, and departmental performance. Extracts from these are given in Figures 9.2, 9.3 and 9.4.

In Figure 9.2, the individual is asked to put a tick in the column which most corresponds to their current performance. The number of ticks in each column is added up. The more ticks in the 'ALWAYS' column, the closer the AP-level to the IP-level. Ticks in other columns indicate areas where more work needs to be done on developing personal quality.

A checklist which can be used to help gain a greater awareness of how others feel about our efforts is shown in Figure 9.3. The individual is asked to put a tick under the number which best expresses how satisfied others are with us. Ten points is the highest score. Some of the people who have to live with the results of our work are also asked to fill out this form, so that we can get an idea of how they feel about our performance.

Figure 9.2   Ideal Performance Level Exercise I

STATEMENT	Always	Mostly	Seldom
1. I perform my tasks as well as I possibly can.		✓	
2. I give myself 100%. I am committed.		✓	
3. I make an extra effort when the situation calls for it.		✓	
4. When the boss is out, I make the same effort as when he/she is there.	✓		
5. When I do a job – large or small – I check it myself to make sure it has been done properly.		✓	
6. I help my colleagues, including those from other departments.			✓
7. I feel responsible for the errors my company makes and I help to correct them, even if I personally did not make them.		✓	
8. I take the initiative to avoid wasting time. When I've finished a job, I find something meaningful to do, or else I ask for new assignments.		✓	
9. When I promise to do a job and deliver a certain standard of quality/quantity on a specific date, I do everything in my power to keep my promise.		✓	
10. I am punctual.		✓	
11. I respect other people's time. If I change my plans or discover that I am going to be late, I let people know at once.			✓
12. I learn from my mistakes, correct them and do not repeat them.		✓	
13. I am proud of my work and am happy to put my name on it.	✓		
14. I clean up after myself and make the place ready for the next person.			✓
15. I try to avoid wasting resources.		✓	
16. I try to make decisions and act as if I was the owner of the company or the person in charge.		✓	
17. I talk **to** others and not **about** them.			✓
18. When people deliver quality work, I praise them.			✓
19. When people deliver work to me which doesn't meet my expectations, I bring it to their attention.			✓
20. I ask for help when I cannot handle a job by myself.		✓	
TOTAL	2	12	6

Figure 9.3 Ideal Performance Level Exercise II

Are you satisfied with my performance?

My quality factors: Those factors which influence how people around me perceive my personal quality	The satisfaction of those around me									
	1	2	3	4	5	6	7	8	9	10
My ability to avoid errors										
My commitment										
My loyalty										
My ability to keep agreements										
My helpfulness and ability to cooperate										
My integrity										
My productivity										
My punctuality										
My flexibility										
My sense of order										
My cost awareness										
My professional competence										
My ability to communicate										
My ability to follow-up										
My tolerance										
My interest in and respect for others										
My personal hygiene										
My self-discipline and perseverance										
The strength of my convictions										

Figure 9.4 Ideal Performance Level Exercise III

No.	How do you evaluate departmental quality in this area?	5	4	3	2	1
1.	**Goals**					
	Are departmental goals clear?					
	Does everyone know them?					
	Are they both realistic and challenging?					
	Are they accepted by everyone?					
	Overall evaluation					
2.	**Sharing of responsibility**					
	Does everyone know exactly what they are responsible for and what is expected of them?					
	Do they know what they can do without asking first?					
	Does each individual understand his or her role in the overall scheme of things?					
	Overall evaluation					
3.	**Effectiveness/efficiency/productivity**					
	Does the department meet the expectations of others with regard to effectiveness and productivity?					
	Are things always done on time, in the agreed quality, and with the least possible use of resources?					
	Is our percentage of error acceptable?					
	Overall evaluation					
4.	**Decision making**					
	Are decisions in the department made at a sensible level?					
	Are decisions made quickly enough?					
	Are decisions based on sufficient information?					
	Overall evaluation					
5.	**Delegation**					
	Is there enough delegation?					
	Are employee skills used to best advantage?					
	Is the method of delegation sensible?					
	Are employees being trained to accept increasingly greater responsibility?					
	Overall evaluation					
6.	**Internal communication and coordination**					
	Do we function as a team?					
	Are we pulling in the same direction?					
	Do we keep each other sufficiently informed?					
	Are our communication methods adequate?					
	Do we hold effective meetings?					
	Do we tell each other when we can be contacted?					
	Do we show respect for one another's time?					
	Overall evaluation					

173

Figure 9.4 shows an extract from a form utilised to evaluate departmental performance.

9.4 THE LISTENING VERSUS TELLING ROLE

In this book, the approach to quality measurement and implementing company-wide improvement through Total Quality Management is discussed. However, this initiative will be of little, or no, value if it is discouraged by lines of demarcation between departments, functions and individuals.

There must be a fundamental change in the style adopted by management if success is to be achieved. Unless we recognise the impact that managers have on those who work for them, and their peers, employees will soon see that little has changed, and their full involvement and co-operation is unlikely to materialise. Some managers will, of course, be very apprehensive at changing their style, since after all, this was not normally the way they were taught. What we are really asking is for the manager to become the coach, or cheer-leader, standing on the touch-line giving help and encouragement, rather than the Sergeant Major approach. Managers should give members of their teams a chance to contribute.

We have to develop a climate where product quality and service can grow and develop together. We need to create an environment where problems are 'owned' rather than passed on, and blaming does not take place provided we learn from the mistakes. Without personal quality there can be no service or product quality.

10. The Complicated Stuff – Run Charts, SPC, Taguchi Methods etc.

10.1 WHY DO WE NEED THE COMPLICATED STUFF?

No book on the measurement of quality would be complete without at least one chapter of complicated formulae, technical jargon, strange and uninterpretable diagrams and a statement to the effect that this paraphernalia is an essential part of the measurement of quality. No book, that is, but this one. At a first look at this chapter you may disagree, but do please read on.

In putting together this book we have deliberately avoided the technical concept of measurement. Our key objective has been to get across the message that not only is measurement essential for a quality improvement programme, it should not be and does not have to have to be complicated. So why then have we included this chapter, that covers the techical side of quality; run charts, statistical process control, Taguchi methods etc? The answer is two-fold. Firstly, if we avoided the area entirely, the reader might not be able to put into context the over-technical literature and practices that he may find on the shop-floor and in the hands of the specialists within his own organisation. Secondly, it is important that we illustrate that even the complicated stuff does not have to be, and should not be, complicated.

Our interest in measurement arises, at least partially, because of the variation that exists in natural processes. This natural background variation makes it hard for us to distinguish real trends or exceptional circumstances that are taking place. Most of the technical side of quality measurement, the complicated stuff, is about identifying exceptional circumstances against the background of natural variation, dealing with such exceptional circumstances, estimating their effect when necessary, understanding the variation and its causes and dealing with it. The tools help us to remove sources of variation, or reduce variation, or create insensitivity or robustness to variation, as well as controlling variation within acceptable limits.

All of this is a very important improvement activity; variation is the enemy of quality, quality is about delivering the expected product or service, to at least the expected and acceptable level of excellence each time, every time. Variation gets in the way of delivering this service. The variation may be in the performance of mechanical or electrical equipment or it may be variation in incoming raw material, possibly outside specification. It may be variation in the environment and, of course, it may be variation in our people. Pursuit of quality is about the elimination of variation; it is our responsibility as managers in a total quality management organisation relentlessly to hunt down unacceptable variation and reduce or remove it. This is the fundamental rationale behind the Motorola Six Sigma programme.

We need the complicated stuff, then, in order to facilitate a proactive, systematic approach to improvement throughout our business processes. The complicated stuff helps us to evaluate the capability of those processes against the requirement, to troubleshoot when the processes go out of control, to verify that the processes are in control and to identify the causal factors that explain the variation in those processes: normal variation and exceptional variation.

The mistake that many have made, is to think that the use of the complicated stuff precludes or take precedence over the simple approaches to measurement that we have already discussed in this book. One should not go directly to the complicated stuff; there are many more important things to do first, but that is the error of many techical specialists. However, the opposite error is also common; managers have been scared by the over-complicated over-complex approach by which some have presented many of the technical tools of quality improvement, and shy away from going the whole hog and introducing these into their business processes. Thus, Statistical Process Control may be employed in manufacturing areas but very rarely in non-manufacturing ones. The complicated stuff should not come first, but it must come. And when we do introduce it, we must introduce it as simply as possible.

10.2 WHY SHOULD IT BE COMPLICATED? – HOW TO SIMPLIFY IT

The truth is that it does not have to be complicated. The complication has arisen from a combination of the academic statistical tradition with the evolution of statistical quality tools in production areas. The assumption of those steeped in the routine use of these tools and methodology is that all the rest of us are steeped in their use too. They do nothing to make the approaches transparent and on occasion they forget why they are using them at all. And, in the background, academics and consultants complicate the issue by concentrating on the *complexity* and not the *simplicity* of the subject matter.

This situation is in direct contrast to the concentration on simplicity and mass use epitomised by the Japanese quality gurus. Ishikawa, Taguchi and Shingo all represent the principles of mass education, of simplified tools utilised throughout the workforce, of learning on the job, and of application on a team basis. Is it any wonder that despite the fact that we have for many years run courses on Statistical Process Control and other statistical quality improvement tools, their actual application in British industry is so limited? Concentrating too much on the statistical niceties, the real implementation problems of organisational and management barriers to change, and the application in the specific technology of one's own organisation, have usually been neglected. The same is true of the classical approach to experimental design. The Japanese approach is, in contrast, to simplify the statistical aspects and concentrate on the application. Ishikawa's seven tools of quality control were so simple that even top management could understand them; they learnt them to use rather than just to be seen to have quality training, or to give lip-service to the need to have quality improvement. The use of simplified tools has the advantages of establishing a common language throughout the organisation; a self-contained minimal set of tools to be used for analysis and presentation, in order to achieve clearer communication and fewer misunderstandings. It assists in the focus of fundamental business problems across the organisation, and in the planning and driving of an improvement process.

The complicated stuff, then, does not need to be complicated. We should deliberately aim to simplify it by removing techical prerequisites in education and the use of jargon, by clarifying its concept and language, by removing the theory behind the methods, and by clarifying and automating them. This is in line with the general Japanese principle of deskilling work in order to reduce variability and increase perfect reproducibility. The crucial thing to remember is that the methods themselves are not complicated. They are simple, we just complicate matters.

10.3 RUN CHARTS AND STATISTICAL PROCESS CONTROL

The basic concept of the run chart was introduced in Chapter 5; an illustration is shown in Figure 10.1. An important characteristic is measured through time, perhaps on the basis of sampling at each point in time an average or other summary value is calculated and plotted, and the points are joined up. Possibly a target value is indicated, showing the target to be reached at a given point in time, and a direction that is desired or a direction of goodness may also be supplied.

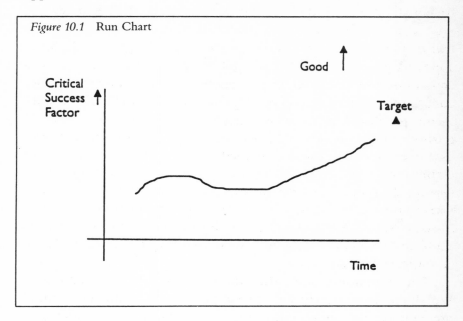

Figure 10.1   Run Chart

Run charts are an excellent way of studying changes in processes, as well as stability. Changes in direction away from the direction of goodness should be carefully monitored and responded to by management.

The basic control chart is a development of the simple run chart. An illustration is shown in Figure 10.2. Here an $\bar{x}$–R chart is shown based on taking samples through time; the means and the range are plotted for each time point. $\bar{x}$ represents the mean and R the range (largest minus smallest) of a sample. Essentially here, then, we have two separate but related run charts with the addition of control limits shown on the graphs. These limits represent a range of normal background variability which we believe appropriate if there is no fundamental change in the process. Going beyond the limits would be a cause for concern since it would show, presumably, that there has been a change in the fundamental business process.

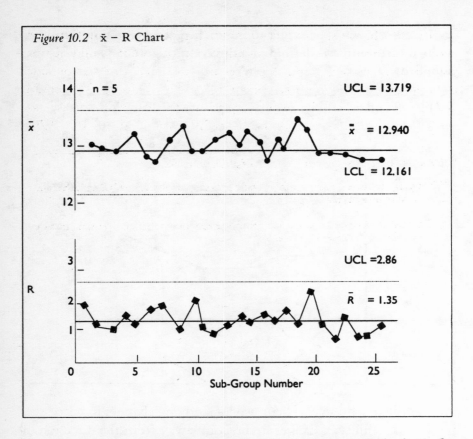

Figure 10.2 x̄ – R Chart

The simple control chart, such as the x̄–R chart, is the basis for the method known as Statistical Process Control or SPC. SPC is a technique which has been known for a long time but its application is still rather limited in many western organisations, where it is often seen as a technique to be utilised on large-scale manufacturing processes. In fact it has enormous potential application on small–scale production, and also in non-manufacturing areas throughout our organisations.

Behind the concept of Statistical Process Control are the two approaches to dealing with variation. The traditional engineering approach to variation was to consider allowable and non–allowable variation; we put up arbitrary tolerances and if we were within those tolerances in our manufacturing processes then we judged the situation to be satisfactoy. We would, for instance, manufacture a product, inspect it to see if it was within the tolerances, and if it was we would then pack it and ship it to our customer. If it was outside the tolerances, we would rework it and either scrap it, if we could not rework it adequately, or put it back into the inspection process as now, we hope, have a good and satisfactory item. In the 1920s

Figure 10.3 The Shewhart Concept of Variation (1920s)

"While every process displays variation, some processes display controlled variation and others display uncontrolled variation."

(a) Controlled variation is a stable and consistent pattern of variation over time that can be attributed to "chance" causes.

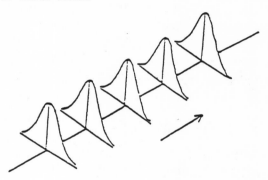

(b) Uncontrolled variation is a changing pattern of variation over time that is attributable to "assignable causes."

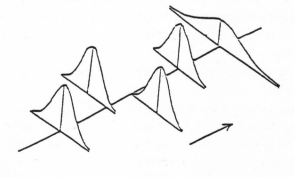

Shewhart introduced another concept of variation, which embodied the belief that whilst every process displays variation, some processes display controlled variation and others uncontrolled variation. This may be illustrated graphically as in Figure 10.3.

Considering the situation in Figure 10.3a we see variation in our machined length or quality characteristic and this stays relatively stable through time. This situation is to be preferred to the alternative in Figure 10.3b in which we have not only changes in location through time, as the mean length of the items changed, but also changes in dispersion as the spread of the items produced changes through time. In this broader concept of variation identified by Shewhart it is no longer necessary to inspect to check conformance to predetermined tolerances, but we have to establish the natural variation inherent in our process and verify if our process is adequate for our requirement. We have to talk about the capability of our process, which is about the relationship between the natural variation and what we require. In this concept of variation, we may have to change our process to achieve our objectives, not just rework our items.

Statistical Process Control then, is the use of small production or other samples to understand and control variation. However, we should concentrate on the process of implementation of statistical process control and not just on the control charts. All too frequently in our factories, we see control charts on the wall, but statistical process control is not really in place. Charts are sometimes constructed for their own sake and do not give a good insight into what is going on in the processes and how we can control them. The application and implementation of statistical process control requires careful planning.

SPC can be applied as a unified approach to high and low volume systems, it can be applied to high and low technology and it is a relatively straightforward universal system. It is for these reasons that the new BS 9000 CECC system for electronic components, based on Technology Approval, is being set up within which SPC is used as the fundamental methodology. It helps us keep control of production and facilitates fast reaction to drift or catastrophic step changes in our processes. We can therefore reduce scrap, reduce rework and reduce inspection delay.

There have been many excuses as to why certain organisations and certain industries have not gone down the route to statistical process control. Some are ignorance, lack of customer requirement, small scale of operation, or small batch sizes. These excuses are no longer tenable; the customer pressure for SPC is great and there are really major benefits to be obtained even in small-scale operation. Another problem with SPC has been that many companies flounder after first application or training. This is because of the concept gap between somewhat theoretical and abstract training courses and the managerial and engineering reality of implementing SPC and running it within your own organisation. Too much emphasis is placed on the statistical niceties and no emphasis on the penetration of a company culture. There is a need to remove attitudinal and motivational barriers as well as organisational ones, and SPC like other quality tools and techniques requires facilitation. Problem solving and troubleshooting using SPC is to some extent skill based.

There are other benefits of SPC; the establishment of the charts in the first place is an improvement activity because critical process steps and parameters are identified, special causes of variation that we do not want are removed, and the capability of the process step is established. As by-products, we get a better understanding of the processes and of the methodology of establishing process operations. Also we get increased management control, in commissioning and set up, but also in predictability and operation. The motivation of the workforce may often improve. Often SPC assists worker involvement because of increased visibility of what is going on and of performance, of improved control and the early diagnosis of problems. It also helps us introduce teams into a culture which they may find a bit strange. Some organisations have used SPC as the route to operator self checking.

SPC, then, is a crucial tool in the TQM armoury and has the added advantage of offering some of the early successes that you need in a TQM programme. It helps understanding, management control, motivation and the introduction of teams. The other, technical tools of quality, to a large extent, do the same.

Let us now consider the implementation steps for SPC. Firstly we have the initial identification, justification and agreeing of the application. We then break the process into steps, identify the critical process steps and parameters, and remove any special causes of variation to establish statistical control. We must then establish the capability of the process steps compared to the specification or requirement, set up the control charts, probably for the mean and range or for attributes to control the process, and monitor performance of the system on an on–going basis.

In this establishment process, various types of training are necessary. We need front-end training for the site manager and the people who are taking engineering responsibility for statistical process control, but we also need training for the supervisors, or perhaps the quality assurance staff, and for the workforce. This training will be virtually on–the–job as statistical process control is implemented in various parts of the processes and the organisation. Figure 10.4 shows an example of breaking a process down into steps. In each of these steps we can identify important parameters that need to be monitored and measured and will be the basis, perhaps, for the implementation of statistical process control.

How do we establish this capability, this comparison of the requirement with the capability of the process or process step we are considering? Clearly if our process is not capable, we have problems. Either we will have to rely on manufacturing some bad product and sorting it out by inspection, and maybe reworking it, or we are going to have to narrow the natural variation in our process step to improve the capability, or we are going to have to widen the specification. While widening the specification is not necessarily desirable in most applications, in many cases the specification has been somewhat arbitrarily set and it may not be necessary to have such a tight tolerance.

There are two simple indexes which do compare the specification with requirement; these are called the Cp and Cpk indexes, which basically compare the allowable process-step spread with the actual process-step spread. The Cp index is the more crude index, being

Figure 10.4   Steps in Wafer Fabrication and Assembly for the Semi
Conductor Industry

WAFER PROCESSING

Metallization/Polysilicon
  Dimension
  Resistivity
Isolation Layers
  Thickness
  Electrical Stability (where appropriate)
  Mechanical Stability (where appropriate)
  Particles
Protective Layers
  Thickness
  Mechanical Stability (where appropriate)
  Particles
Photolithographic Characterization
  Threshold voltage
  Critical dimensions
  Gain
  Breakdown Voltages

ASSEMBLY

Die Bonding
  Die Shear
  Epoxy Void
  Adhesive Layer Thickness
Wire Bonding
  Bond Strength
  Wire Pull Strength
  Ball Size
  Ball Shear Strength
  Ball Placement
Lead Forming and Finishing
  Tin Layer Thickness
  Coplanarity
  Seating Height

simply the difference between the upper specification limit and the lower specification limit divided by the natural spread of the distribution, which is taken to be six times the standard deviation as in Figure 10.5. The measure has one fundamental disadvantage, in that it does not allow for a displacement of the process or its mean away from the target. The Cpk index enables that to be taken into account. The Cpk index is a more complex index, looking at the minimum of the distance from either the upper specification limit to the mean of the process, or the lower specification limit to the mean of the process and dividing that figure by the natural process step spread, in this case three times the standard deviation.

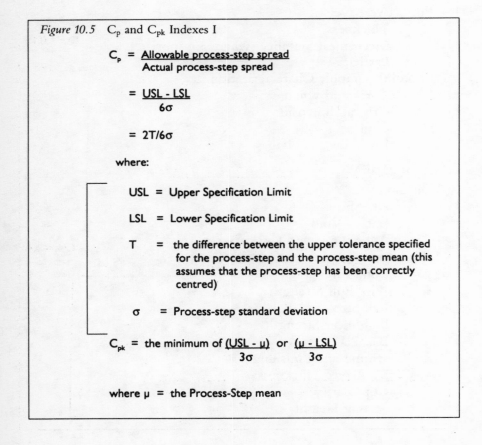

Figure 10.5 C_p and C_{pk} Indexes I

$$C_p = \frac{\text{Allowable process-step spread}}{\text{Actual process-step spread}}$$

$$= \frac{\text{USL - LSL}}{6\sigma}$$

$$= 2T/6\sigma$$

where:

USL = Upper Specification Limit

LSL = Lower Specification Limit

T = the difference between the upper tolerance specified for the process-step and the process-step mean (this assumes that the process-step has been correctly centred)

σ = Process-step standard deviation

$$C_{pk} = \text{the minimum of } \frac{(\text{USL} - \mu)}{3\sigma} \text{ or } \frac{(\mu - \text{LSL})}{3\sigma}$$

where μ = the Process-Step mean

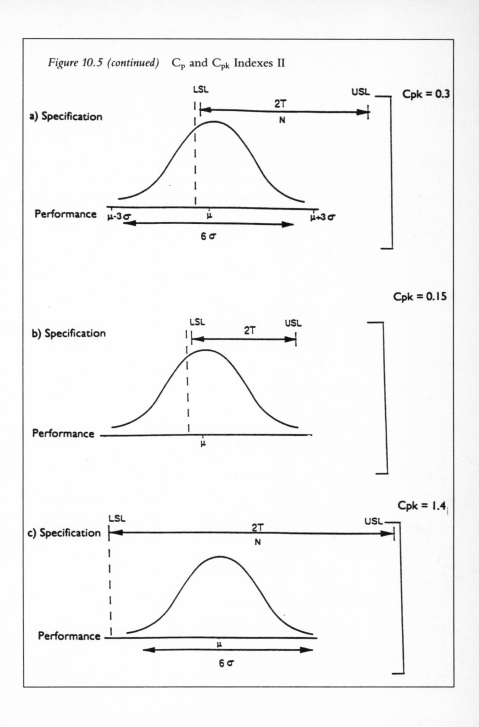

Figure 10.5 (continued) C_p and C_{pk} Indexes II

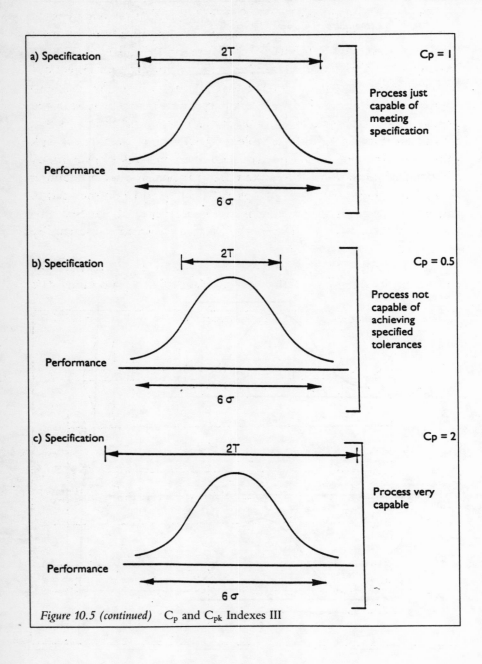

Figure 10.5 (continued) C_p and C_{pk} Indexes III

The great advantages of the Cpk index is that it enables us to compare, throughout our processes and our organisation, how far we have gone down the road of continuous improvement. By looking at the Cpk value we can see whether our processes meet our requirements and what we have to do about them. We can also compare our ability to meet requirements in different processes and process–steps. Cpk or Cp values below one, represent processes that are not capable. To be fully capable we are looking, perhaps, at Cpk values and Cp values of about two. And many process–steps in many advanced organisations have gone much further, and we are talking about Cpk values of 3, 4, 5, 6. Cpk is a driving force on the road to continuous improvement and is a cornerstone of quality improvement programmes such as the Six Sigma programme run by Motorola.

On the simplest and most basic control chart, the $\bar{x}$–R chart, the control limits on the chart have been established by previous data

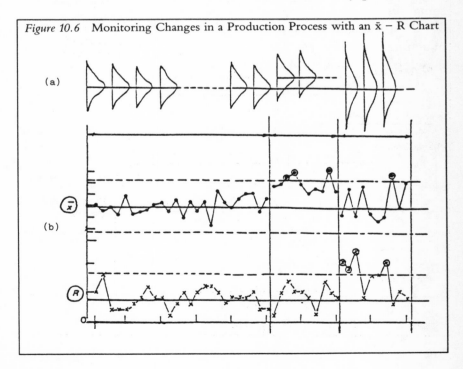

Figure 10.6 Monitoring Changes in a Production Process with an $\bar{x}$ – R Chart

investigations based on collecting information, and we need to ensure that the process is stable and capable before we do this. Once the $\bar{x}$–R chart has been estalbished, we may use it to spot any peculiarities or abnormalities that arise in controlling the process. In Figure 10.6a, for example, we have a shift of mean: perhaps suddenly the process had changed, or it may be gradual change. How can you spot this on the control chart?

If the average of the process – for example the average length of bars being produced – changes, this should affect the mean and we would expect to find points drifting outside the limits on the mean chart. The range is hardly affected at all. If, on the other hand, machine variation changes, it would show primarily on the range chart, and possibly to a lesser extent on the mean chart (Figure 10.6b). These changes may be due to machines in which parts break, drift out of calibration or in which some external source comes into to disturb the process; perhaps incoming raw materials have become contaminated or we have started a new batch.

The mean and range chart can also be used to identify the types of abnormality. The most basic types of abnormality for which you may look are shown in Figure 10.7.

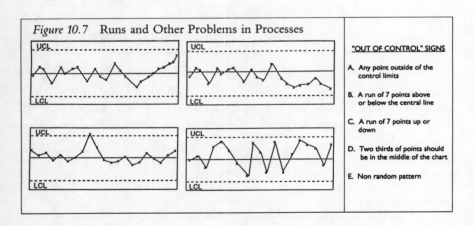

Figure 10.7   Runs and Other Problems in Processes

"OUT OF CONTROL" SIGNS

A. Any point outside of the control limits

B. A run of 7 points above or below the central line

C. A run of 7 points up or down

D. Two thirds of points should be in the middle of the chart

E. Non random pattern

If we get a run of seven or more points above or below the central line this would seem to indicate that there is something strange happening in the process, perhaps a shift of mean. If we get a run of seven points continuously going up or down it would appear that we have reached a situation in which something systematic is happening. We should also expect two thirds of the points to be in the middle one third of the chart and if this is not happening it could well be indicating bad instrumentation or something wrong in the process. Again, regular cycles or patterns would be indicating to us that we are missing something in our study of the process and that we should really be taking this regular cycle into account.

As well as $\bar{x}$–R charts, there are other types of control charts regularly used in the control of processes, both in manufacturing and in non-manufacturing areas. These charts are associated with the study of attributes, to the presence or absence of defects or whether a part is defective or not. Various types of attribute charts are available. Statistical Process Control, then, is not just about constructing control charts; but control charts are the central tool of the methodology and they must be properly used.

10.4 TAGUCHI METHODS AND DESIGN OF EXPERIMENTS

Taguchi methodology is essentially about pushing quality back to the design stage where it really belongs. However much you inspect a product, if the design is bad, you are still going to have a lot of scrap and a lot of rework and occasionally a poor product going out into the field. As utilised in Japan, Taguchi methods are about routinely optimising both product and processes prior to moving into the manufacturing phase. However, in the West they are often used in troubleshooting on production lines. This is the way many companies learn to understand the methods and eventually to push them back to the design area. The basic message of Taguchi is that you need to design and produce robust products, capable of withstanding the manufacturing process.

It is a prototyping method, similar in structure to other, older engineering techniques: Failure Modes and Effects Analysis (FMEA) and Fault-Tree analysis. Its power can be best understood by utilising a quote from Toyota. According to Toyota 50 per cent of design improvement comes from Taguchi methodology, 35 per cent comes from FMEA and 15 per cent from Fault-Tree analysis. Taguchi then, is the key player in the design improvement process.

Methods like Taguchi have been around in British and world industry for many years but, unfortunately, have never become widely applied. The reasons for this were that they were not well adjusted to manufacturing and design processes and were not presented in such a way as to make them relatively easy to teach to a wide audience. Instead you had to be a statistical expert, a technocrat, who then, perhaps because of his jargon, could not communicate very well with the rest of the organisation. The result of this was that these statistical methods, though very well founded, never really took off within organisations. Taguchi has created a breakthrough in experimental design by packaging the approach in a very easy, simple to use package. Not as easy as the seven tools of quality control, but certainly a lot simpler than previous approaches that had been developed by statisticians rather than engineers.

One question associated with the application of the Taguchi methods is the rather familiar one – Aren't we doing it already? Are we perhaps doing it under another name? The answer to this question generally will be no, and there is plenty of evidence to show why that is the case. Anyone who works in design knows about those design disasters which never quite got to the public's attention. (There have been one or two public ones as well, for instance the Advanced Passenger Train.) If you look at quality and reliability data, in the first couple of years of field life of a new system there are typically failure modes which then disappear from the records. These have been designed out in the field, at a rather high cost.

The usual reason why we are not utilising Taguchi methods already, is the way in which we tend to think about design, as a very skilled job, something you learn at a designer's knee. The Japanese, typically, have deskilled aspects of this job, so that where possible they can be done routinely. One way to think about this is to consider a design–space, and put into a box bits of paper carrying all the different potential designs which can produce the functionality

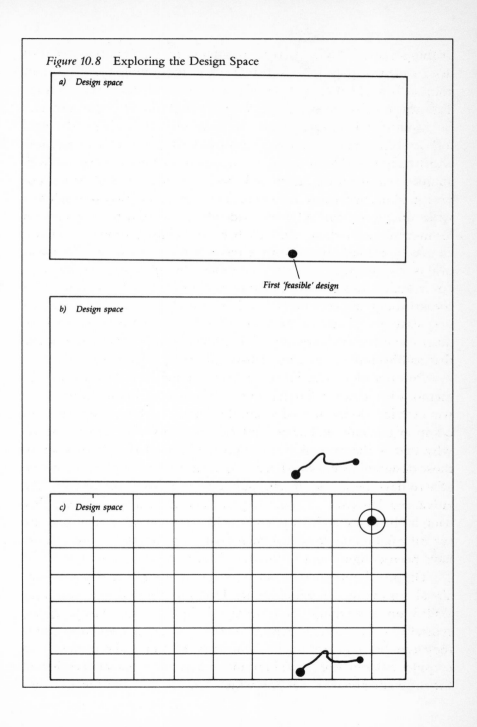

Figure 10.8   Exploring the Design Space

a)   *Design space*

First 'feasible' design

b)   *Design space*

c)   *Design space*

required by a customer, as in Figure 10.8. Perhaps the customer requirement is for a table which the customer thinks of functionally as a flat surface a certain height above the floor with certain dimensions of flatness and capable of withstanding a certain load. Typically, the first design would be somewhat marginal and we need to twiddle aspects of the design–change the leg configuration, change the materials – in order to get the design to a satisfactory state. Very frequently, the only reason we are meeting the specification is because it is inadequately defined. Perhaps we have not pointed out that this table needs to be manoeuvrable, so that it cannot be made in concrete. If the true optimum design is some way away from the area in which we have been developing our design, then there is no reason why we will necessarily trip over it in this process and, anyway, we tend to stop because we have run out of resources, not because the design is perfect.

The exact analogue, of course, occurs in the production area. Here we have a production space. Onto the bits of paper we put different ways of running the production process; it could be machine speeds, temperature settings, different material choices, and so on. When the line is first up and running, it is more often limping – we cannot get the throughput, or the quality level, or the machine keeps breaking down. Again, we have to twiddle the important parameters and eventually we stop because we run out of resources, or because we have reduced the failure rate or the defect rate, without knowing quite why or how, and therefore we do not want to carry on.

The Taguchi approach, in contrast, is to define the limits of the design or production space and systematically search it and, unlike other statistical methods, it does this in a minimum number of prototypes, which makes the technique practical. There has been considerable criticism of Taguchi's methods in the United States, but this has tended to be associated with one interpretation of his package. Taguchi's approach to quality is based on methodology developed, largely in the United Kingdom, around the period of the Second World War. These approaches, known as experimental design methods, and analysis of variance methods (ANOVA for short) have been used world-wide in all kinds of experiments, from agricultural to biological, from marketing to industrial. They are essentially about the difference between comparative and demonstration tests. Many people in industry kid themselves that they are doing demonstration tests. 'We will just try this, and if it works we will sign it off'. It does not quite work, and so we need to change it, and change it again, and by the time we have made a few changes we might have done better to have gone for systematic comparative testing in the first place.

The development of the methods in the United Kingdom was associated with Sir R.A. Fisher who spent the Second World War at the Rothamstead Agricultural Research Establishment working on experiments to improve food yield. Fisher used his field at Rothamstead for experimentation on crops. He would divide the field up into cells or plots. In Figure 10.9, for example, different

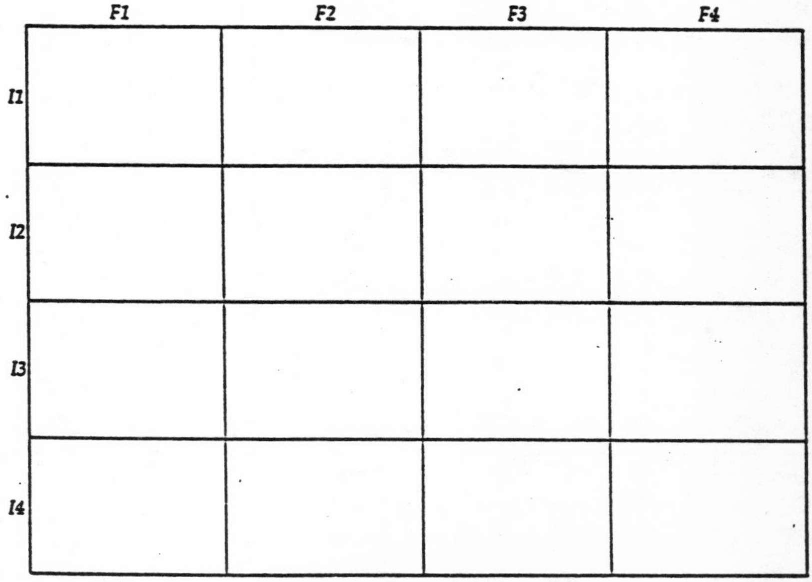

Figure 10.9   Fisher's Field – a full factorial experiment

fertilisers are in the columns and different irrigation levels in the rows, and the wheat output per acre from each of the combinations is being measured. This is a very inefficient experiment, because all combinations are utilised. If we can cut down the number of combinations, we can dramatically reduce the amount of necessary experimentation.

This is particularly feasible in industrial rather than agricultural experiments, as Taguchi realised, because in industrial experiments we can always go back and check, while in agriculture it would take an extra year because of the annual agricultural cycle. Indeed, in forestry, it often takes fifty years! This reliance on the confirmatory experiment, as Taguchi calls it, enables work to be done with minimum numbers of prototypes.

Taguchi tabulated in a standard set of tables (the various so–called Orthogonal Arrays), experimental designs to be utilised in optimising a product design, a process design, a process calibration or in troubleshooting in the production process. The L_4 design in Figure 10.10 enables us to look at three factors, three variables which

Figure 10.10 L_4 Orthogonal Array

Trial \ Factor	A	B	C
1	1	1	1
2	1	2	2
3	2	1	2
4	2	2	1

may be affecting the process; perhaps a machine speed, a temperature, a material. Each of these can have two options, two levels. Two times two times two would give us eight combinations, but we have halved the number of prototypes using the Taguchi

Orthogonal Array. As shown in Figure 10.11, the L_8 enables us to look at up to seven such factors in eight instead of 128 trials. The L_9 enables us to look at four three level factors in nine instead of 81

Figure 10.11   Common Orthogonal Arrays

	No. of factors and levels	No. of trials in full factorial
L_4	3×2 levels	(8)
L_8	7×2 levels	(128)
L_9	4×3 levels	(81)
L_{12}	11×2 levels	(2,048)
L_{16}	15×2 levels	(32,768)
L_{18}	1×2 levels	
	7×3 levels	(4,374)
L_{25}	6×5 levels	(15,625)
L_{27}	13×3 levels	(1,594,323)
L_{32}	31×2 levels	(2,000m)
L_{36}	3×2 levels	
	13×3 levels	(12.7m)
L_{50}	1×2 levels	
	11×5 levels	(97.6m)
L_{54}	1×2 levels	
	25×3 levels	($1.7m^2$)
etc.		

trials. We have 12 instead of about 2,000 in L_{12}; we have 16 instead of 33,000 in the L_{16}; 18 instead of 4,500; 25 instead of 15,500 and 27 instead of 1.5 million. Very few people make up 1.5 million prototypes, at least deliberately!

The L_{54} is the largest industrial experiment run personally by one of the authors. This was a major troubleshoot based on eight days of two twelve-hour shifts, to turn around a £2 million product line, which after 18 months commissioning could not make anything. Fifty-four trials instead of 1.7 million were used over eight days, obviously a major saving!

In the L_9 orthogonal array in Figure 10.12, there are four factors

Figure 10.12 L_9 Orthogonal Array				
Factor Experimental trial or prototype	A	B	C	D
1	1	1	1	1
2	1	2	2	2
3	1	3	3	3
4	2	1	2	3
5	2	2	3	1
6	2	3	1	2
7	3	1	3	2
8	3	2	1	3
9	3	3	2	1

A, B, C and D – A may be a machine speed, B may be a temperature setting, C may be a pressure setting and D may be a material choice (three alternative materials). According to the Orthogonal Array, the first trial is to be run with the lowest machine speed, the lowest temperature, the lowest pressure and the first material, and we continue in this way until in the last trial we have the highest machine speed, highest temperature, middle pressure and the first material. In all of these nine trials, we measure the quality characteristics that matter the most to us; perhaps it is the throughput, perhaps it is the quality standard of the items or, indeed, it may be the length.

Taguchi methodology is fundamentally evolutionary like many other statistical approaches; having run one small experiment we review our findings and go on to the next experiment to improve further. We perhaps zoom in on the factor levels as we learn more about the importance of certain factors.

Perhaps the hardest concept associated with Taguchi is the concept of noise. The factors we have considered so far may be called control factors; these are factors which in normal production we can actually manipulate; they may be design features, they may be production variables such as temperature and machine speed. They are accessible to us to change. Noise factors in contrast, are factors which in test we may be able to control but in production we cannot. These are the fluctuations in performance of individuals, fluctuations in raw materials within specification (or indeed outside specification if we are not checking), and fluctuations in the environment. These fluctuations cause the transients in our production processes.

Figure 10.13 Parameter Design with Control and Noise Factors

NOISE FACTORS

	4	3	2	1	Factor / Trial
	2	2	1	1	A
	2	1	2	1	B
	1	2	2	1	C

$L_9 \times L_4 = 36$

CONTROL FACTORS

$(3^4 \times 2^3 = 648)$

Trial \ Factor	A	B	C	D					
1	1	1	1	1	O	O	O	O	
2	1	2	2	2	O	O	O	O	Data
3	1	3	3	3	O	O	O	O	matrix
4	2	1	2	3	O	O	O	O	
5	2	2	3	1	O	O	O	O	
6	2	3	1	2	O	O	O	O	
7	3	1	3	2	O	O	O	O	
8	3	2	1	3	O	O	O	O	
9	3	3	2	1	O	O	O	O	

In Figure 10.13 we have a matrix of control factors which is the L_9 orthogonal array, and we also have a matrix of noise factors, which here is an L_4 orthogonal array turned on its side. Noise factors represent the disturbances we will meet in production, and in order to verify that we have chosen the best design, or indeed the best setting, what we need to do is to check that setting over various noise combinations. Here, then, we duplicate our control setting over the four noise combinations generated by the L_4. Our aim is to ensure that we choose the control setting that gives us the right answer on average across the noise combinations, and the least spread, the least difference caused by the noise. We can do this by finding one of the control combinations which gives us the right mean on average, but also a small standard deviation.

Taguchi combines the mean and standard deviation into a measure called the Signal to Noise ratio. This has been an area of some criticism of the Taguchi approach, but it does allow us to find out very quickly and easily which of our long list of possible control factors really affects the quality measures that we are interested in. We can then go back and find out whether it is the mean that is affected or the consistency over various noise combinations. Various formulas for the Signal to Noise ratio have been put up, corresponding to the smallest is best situation, the biggest is best situation and the nominal is best situation.

To summarise so far, Taguchi minimises variation. He has a system of orthogonal arrays which allows quick and easy identification of the appropriate experimental designs. Whilst we have not dealt with it, this system of orthogonal arrays also allows us to incorporate various interactions or non-linearities into the analysis. It is evolutionary and it explicitly treats noise factors and minimises the sensitivity to noise.

Another advantage is that it enables us to give relatively simplistic graphical results as in Figure 10.14. This corresponds to a pick and place robot arm placing surface mounted components on circuit boards, unfortunately often crooked. In this commissioning experiment, the aim is to get those components down as straight as possible; brainstorming has identified five control variables; the speed of convergence of the jaws, the pressure of squeezing of jaws A and of jaws B, the placement force and the tweezer mode (whether it is the narrow then wide tweezers or the both-together mode).

We see immediately the outputs of a Taguchi analysis. Firstly, we get the optimum design features or process settings; here we need to choose the slower speed of convergence of the jaws, 45 psi for the

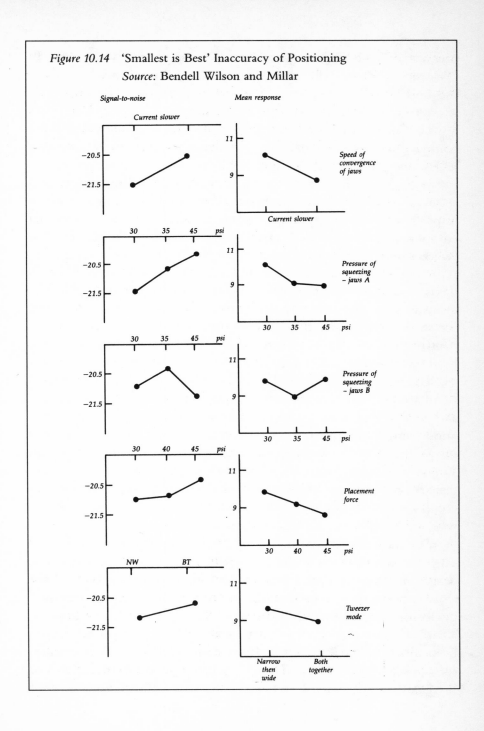

Figure 10.14 'Smallest is Best' Inaccuracy of Positioning
Source: Bendell Wilson and Millar

pressure of squeezing for jaws A and 35 psi, strangely, for jaws B. We need to choose a placement force of 45 psi and we need to choose the both-together tweezer mode, although it does not appear to make too much difference.

The second thing we gain is the importance of variables. If we compare the first and the last graph because they both have two levels, we can see that the speed of convergence of the jaws has a much greater gradient than the tweezer mode, and since the vertical scales are the same this implies that the tweezer mode is not as important. If we are mixing product on the line, and for another component type the alternative tweezer mode is better and the tweezer mode is hard to reset, then we might not bother to change it. If, on the other hand, the speed of convergence of the jaws shifts, if it tends to drift for example, then we may have a serious problem in terms of the inaccuracy of positioning. This is an indicator of where we should apply statistical process control; here we could install a control loop in order to ensure that the speed of the convergence is monitored and is in fact kept to about the right level.

The third advantage of Taguchi methods is the highlighting of peculiarities. Here, for instance, the pressure of squeezing of jaws A and jaws B appears to be very different. In fact 35 psi might seem a good compromise for jaws A as well as for jaws B, but, looking at the Signal to Noise analysis, we see that this would be dangerous. Whilst the mean inaccuracy would not be very different, the dispersion would be and so we should get some very badly placed components on occasion. What has gone wrong here is, in fact, a programming error; we discuss this later.

The stage of Taguchi analysis we have talked about so far is what Taguchi himself calls Parameter Design. It can be applied to the design of a product, of a process, or indeed to the calibration and troubleshooting of a production process. Before this we have the genius of creating the 'up and limping' prototype in the first place. That is System Design. It is what we in the West, traditionally, have been much better at than the Japanese have. Following Parameter Design we have Tolerance Design, which will only be necessary, on the Japanese principle of invest last, if when we have gone through our Parameter Design we have not, in fact, reduced the variation in the output characteristics sufficiently.

Taguchi methodology was developed in Japan in the 1960s

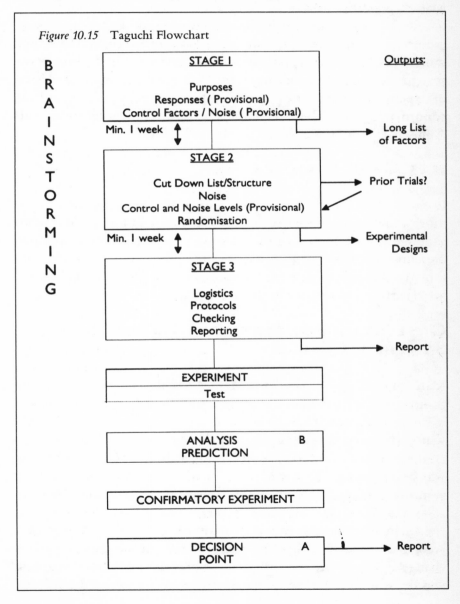

Figure 10.15 Taguchi Flowchart

onwards and hit the United States in the early 1980s; it appeared in Europe from about 1985 onwards. The methods are utilised by such organisations as ITT, Ford, AT & T, Xerox, Lucas and many more. Many applications have been in the automotive and electronics industry, but there are applications in diverse areas including process industries, information technology, food technology and many more. The practical application of Taguchi methods requires a structured discipline involving team brainstorming and then design of experiment, conduct of experiment, analysis, prediction and the confirmatory trial. This is a complex process and requires some skill. A flowchart for application is shown in Figure 10.15.

10.5 CASE STUDIES

In this section we provide some examples of the application of the more complex measurement methodologies. Ironically, there is no shortage of case studies of the application of the more complicated measurement tools of quality. The difficulty is in identifying well thought through, well founded applications which reflect the need for clarity and simplicity in the approach.

CASE STUDY 1: MARCONI DEFENCE SYSTEMS LIMITED

Marconi Defence Systems Ltd (MDSL) has always been a multi-site company. The main Manufacturing Unit is based at Portsmouth and it has provided the main Production facility to the Design Groups which are based at other geographic locations.

During the mid 1980s the drive towards competitive tendering was being pursued by the Ministry of Defence which was then the company's main customer, and the move away from the relatively cosy world of Cost Plus MOD contracts had started.

As in many companies at that time, the need to change was recognised, the historic 'finished product' error strategy had to change and the more productive error prevention mode of working was the new aim, with the emphasis towards controlling the process.

The road to change was not easy, but at the Production Unit in Portsmouth – under the direction of a new and enlightened General Manager – they developed a manufacturing strategy capable of addressing the changes needed.

An analysis of the production business identified the critical processes and these formed the basis of the initial Quality Improvement drive.

The new strategy created Operating Modules, each being a mini-focused factory made up of a number of multi-disciplined Cells. The whole strategy was strongly championed by the General Manager who demonstrated his commitment daily to everybody.

The primary skills of each Cell were matched to the specific phase of the manufacturing process for which they were responsible, i.e. Material Supply through to Piece Part manufacture requiring high manufacturing and Quality Control skills. The Assembly Integration and Test through to delivery required high project management and system skills. (This basic concept remains today, albeit modified slightly).

Each of these Cells was given specific and common terms of reference:

1. Monitor Scrap and Rework
2. Measure and Record Inventory Levels
3. Introduce SPC and Trend Analysis
4. Improve Housekeeping
5. Monitor and Understand the 'Process'
6. Maintain Sales

Item 6 was of paramount importance, as up to that time the Production Unit had always achieved its sales forecasts. The overall approach was to be 'softly softly', the rate of change being managed carefully, with new systems and procedures brought in only when fully proven.

During that time such terms as SPC were relatively alien to most people, and those employees and managers who thought they had any level of understanding could at best be described as being extremely sceptical about their application to the business. The company was at that time producing Defence Systems of generally low volume, very high mix, and of a highly complex technical nature. Such phrases as 'well it's OK in the car industry but it won't work here' could often be heard around both the shop floor and offices.

Once set up, the Cells were provided with on-line training in data collection and chart monitoring techniques to provide regular reports to the Module Management Teams. Each Module Management Team reported to the Executive Steering Committee on a regular basis via Management Presentations. The training and awareness seminars were extensive during this phase as all levels of management and supervision were exposed to new techniques, approaches and thought processes.

All elements of the Production Unit were then focused in the same direction and were all reporting against the same criteria. There were initially 22 operating Cells covering all of the company's main activities/projects.

Statistical Process Control

The introduction of SPC was one crucial aspect of the Cells' terms of reference. The introduction of SPC to the operation basically fell into five phases which followed on from establishment of the Manufacturing Strategy:

Phase I Introduce the workforce to charts and graphs – Sept 1987
Phase II Firm-up on format and content – Jan–Sept 1988
Phase III Introduce quality overview – April 1989
Phase IV Closing the loop – Jan 1990
Phase V Extend the philosophy into Design – Feb 1990 onwards

Phase I – Introducing the Workforce to Charts and Graphs

Within MDSL they had for many years developed a Non-Conformance Data Collection system as a requirement of AQAP registration. This system required each defect/incident 'arising' to be recorded on Defect/Incident Reports which were then collated by the

Quality Department for subsequent analysis. The system was very comprehensive and capable of providing very detailed reports each quarter, with additional six monthly and annual summaries of defect trends. At the touch of a button they could identify what had gone wrong, how many related cases etc., etc., three months ago, six months ago, a year ago. However, trying to find out what had gone wrong yesterday was perhaps another story!

The move was to provide 'real time', current not historic, indicators. The intention was also to extend the collection of data well beyond the manufacturing and Test/Inspection process and into the service departments. Each team was presented with an Attribute Chart and then in discussion identified nine elements of their process which 'always' went wrong. Using the Team's gut feelings they established a 10 Attribute Chart. (The tenth being the miscellaneous attribute to cover any missed.) Tick sheets were developed and the Teams then continued their process and monitored trends and 'arisings'. Some teams obviously 'cottoned on' quicker than others and these were quick to take ownership and develop their charts – and as a result, their processes also.

These flagships were then used to advertise the successes, working on the adage 'Success breeds Success'. The initial flagship proved to be the 'In Circuit Test' facility and every opportunity was taken to 'exploit' its success; it became a prime target for all visitors.

During this phase SPC rules were also established for the company:

No Monitoring without Recording
No Recording without Analysis
No Analysis without Action
No Improvement without Error Cause Removal
and finally
No Gain without Pain

Phase II – Firm-up on Format and Content
As the Teams had been allowed to go with their own versions for

some time, they had become used to filling in charts, recording achievements and reporting their progress.

Now was the time to refine the process and firm up on the chart format, the content, and to formalise the procedure. Up to this stage involvement had been almost optional, driven by peer pressure, and on a very friendly easy-going basis. Again, any improvements identified were readily advertised to one and all, and there was a high level of visible support from the management, created and maintained by the need for report back.

Phase III – Introduce Central Quality Overview

The company was now approaching the point in the programme for 'turning the screw'. Each chart was registered on to Central Quality's data base. This defined the process monitored, the process owner, the Departmental Manager/Project and where necessary the relevant engineering departmental representative.

Central Quality viewed the charts regularly each week and stamped any out of control conditions noted, at the same time issuing a Corrective Action Request Form. These were date/timed on to the data base and the responses recorded and monitored accordingly. Such levels of response, participation, trends etc. were correlated across the site and additionally the effectiveness of corrective and preventative actions was monitored.

Once a chart was logged on to the system it then had to remain in existence unless agreement to discontinue its use was reached between the Departmental Manager and the Unit Quality Manager. SPC now had teeth and the screws could start to be turned. What started out as an 'optional friendly exercise' rapidly became a powerful mandatory tool. However, data collection itself is of no use unless analysis and actions follow.

Phase IV – Closing the Loop

To enable the Cells to identify Failure Modes and achieve error cause removal, training in problem solving techniques was provided. Cause and Effect Analysis, FMEA, brainstorming, Pareto analysis etc. were used. The subsequent analysis of trends and causes with the ensuing improvement activities provided the case studies with which to approach the company's next phase – extending SPC into Design.

Phase V – Extending the Philosophy into Design

This was probably the most difficult phase and is still being developed today. Several prototype schemes are running, the latest of which utilises the output of the standard software development tests, Fagan Inspections, of the company's software products, and the identification of measurable attributes coming from their regular Product Verification Audit programmes.

The experience gained within Production has proved to be invaluable within the overall approach to quality improvement. This in conjunction with some Quality Cost Analysis provided a conclusive case to the MDSL board of directors totally to underwrite and commit to a companywide Total Quality Management Programme.

The Current Status

The areas and disciplines involved in SPC cover the total Manufacturing process as per the Flow Diagram in Figure 10.16.

The response and effectiveness, however, does vary from area to area and from group to group, in the main being dependent upon the local area management and the priority applied. The overall activity has been the subject to a degree of ebb and flow as senior management changes have taken place, but the main direction has been maintained throughout.

Some Achievements To Date

Some of the Marconi Defence Systems achievements to date resulting from Management by Measurement, process recognition, operator ownership of quality and error cause removal:

- Goods Inwards load *reduced* from 1,500 Groups to 147. The target is below 50.
- Production Control System Data input delays of 12 days average *reduced* to 48 hours. The target is four hours.

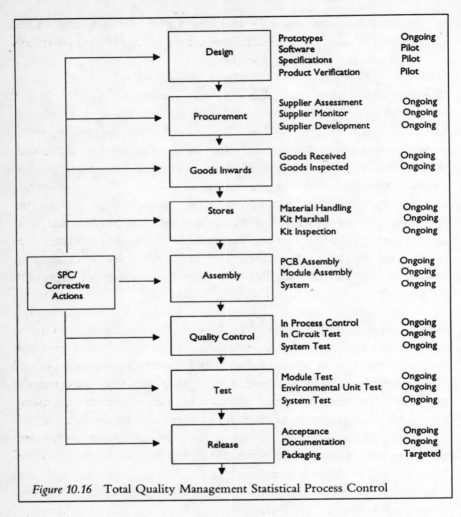

Design	Prototypes	Ongoing
	Software	Pilot
	Specifications	Pilot
	Product Verification	Pilot
Procurement	Supplier Assessment	Ongoing
	Supplier Monitor	Ongoing
	Supplier Development	Ongoing
Goods Inwards	Goods Received	Ongoing
	Goods Inspected	Ongoing
Stores	Material Handling	Ongoing
	Kit Marshall	Ongoing
	Kit Inspection	Ongoing
Assembly	PCB Assembly	Ongoing
	Module Assembly	Ongoing
	System	Ongoing
Quality Control	In Process Control	Ongoing
	In Circuit Test	Ongoing
	System Test	Ongoing
Test	Module Test	Ongoing
	Environmental Unit Test	Ongoing
	System Test	Ongoing
Release	Acceptance	Ongoing
	Documentation	Ongoing
	Packaging	Targeted

SPC/ Corrective Actions

Figure 10.16 Total Quality Management Statistical Process Control

- Time to identify rejects at Goods Inwards of 8 weeks *reduced* to two days. The target is four hours.
- Defective supplies as received *reduced* from 13.3 per cent to 4 per cent. The target is 0.27 per cent.
- Error-rate in kits issued *reduced* from 50 per cent to 11 per cent. The target is 1.4 per cent
- Printed Circuit Board assembly error rate *reduced* from two defects per board to 0.25 per board. The target is 0.025.

- On current commercial product lines the company now measures error rates in Parts Per Million (PPM) and currently are achieving 24 PPM for these lines.

Case Study 2 – TSB

The TSB Retail Banking and Insurance Division provides an excellent example of how even apparently complicated concepts can be applied in a non-manufacturing environment.

TSB began its Total Quality Management Process in 1991, initiated by Peter Ellwood, its Chief Executive. Initially, three line managers were trained in Florida for three months and these subsequently passed on their training to a further 1,000 top managers via a series of four-day courses. By early 1993 the quality training will have been cascaded to all 25,000 employees, as part of a carefully structured training programme.

David Owen, Human Resources and Quality Director, has overall responsibility for the £20 million initiative and sees training as the essential first step towards improving the Quality of Service that TSB provides for its seven million customers through its network of 1,400 retail branches. TSB measures its success by monitoring the reduction of dissatisfaction among customers and measuring discontent compared with the level of complaints against rivals.

For quality improvement, emphasis is placed on good data collection, customer–focused measurement, the display of data and the removal of the root causes of problems. Improvement activities are co-ordinated by 17 local Steering Groups which report to Quality Director Dr. Roger Cliffe. As part of the Total Business Strategy, best practices from the diverse operations within the banking group are collated and communicated to other areas of the business.

Here we shall concentrate on just two examples of the application of SPC concepts within the TSB banking business.

External Sales
The first example concerns the External Sales Department at TSB's Card and Central Services. This has evolved – through TSB Direct –

from UDT Consumer Finance. David Goggin, the Department Manager, has a wealth of experience of using SPC and finds it an ideal management tool to aid improvement efforts.

One application that has been recently introduced relates to the system for processing preferential loans. These are offered to members of subscribing groups, such as trade unions and certain companies. Analysis of customer concerns showed that there were some opportunities to improve turnaround time of applications.

Using a *control chart* it was discovered that 34 per cent of delays were due to the incorrect completion of the documentation by customers. In response to this, a series of procedural changes were introduced to help overcome these delays, e.g. customers are now telephoned rather than written to when a problem occurs. Continued SPC measurement has shown that, by the end of the trial period in July 1991, the average turnaround time had been reduced to 13.5 days. The good news does not end there; SPC has revealed other common problems, such as the lack of proof of income in 33 per cent of applications. These will be tackled in order of priority, going for the 'big and easy problems' in the first instance. The conversion rate from applications to loans has now increased significantly.

SPC was introduced here rather differently to other areas of Card and Central Services. Because of relocation, many staff were new to the Department and not familiar with SPC. Time constraints meant that there was not time to involve fully all staff in the measurement process, and so it was very much management-led and implemented. However, care was taken to ensure that the results were fed back to staff involved in the process and the charts are prominently displayed on the office walls: the more general benefits were readily apparent to all staff. Nevertheless, there is always a danger in such an approach that staff will not take ownership of the improvement process: as with other problems highlighted throughout this book, only consistent management practice can address this issue.

This particular application of SPC also revealed how useful it can be in preventing errors from recurring. In March 1991, a number of 'adjustments' were made to the process. This had an immediately detrimental effect, shown on the charts, and the intended 'process improvements' were withdrawn quickly.

David Goggin stresses the need for managers – or other staff responsible for interpreting the data collected on a control chart – to be fully aware of the day-to-day environment affecting a process. For instance, a high sickness rate on a particular day will inevitably be reflected on the control chart but it would be wrong to over-react and start looking for other causes. The message here must be to look beyond the obvious – ensure the root cause of a problem is being addressed. As with many aspects of SPC, this reflects nothing other than good management practice.

As in the other case studies, a whole range of supporting tools – such as process mapping and the cause/effect diagram – have been used to support SPC. Most importantly, all support work has been tailored to suit specific applications: a 'standard' implementation was not considered to be practical.

Having used SPC so widely in his own job, David Goggin can see SPC helping branch managers to reduce queuing times at their counters, by isolating the reasons for particular delays.

TSB Homeloans

The second example concerns the application of SPC at TSB Homeloans, where the need to understand and improve key work-processes has been a driving influence. From the very first management meeting, measurement of work processes has been regarded as essential. SPC was seen as a way of ensuring that measurement was carried out in an effective and consistent manner.

SPC began in Homeloans in June 1991. The aim was to identify and measure the 'key parameters' of the processes which were 'contributing the largest amount to the total Price of Non-Conformance ... and to implement actions to improve performance'. It was also agreed that SPC would be renamed Process Improvement Charting (PIC) so as to 'avoid frightening staff and to better reflect the emphasis on process improvement'. Homeloans emphasise that they are still in the early stages of introducing PIC.

To start with, the context in which PIC was introduced was seen as crucial: for PIC to work, it had to be trusted, accepted and owned by all process operators. This was achieved by marketing the new process: emphasis was placed on the internal customer/supplier relationship and the charts were introduced as an opportunity to 'tell management where the problems are'. A commitment was made to feed back and act upon the results of the measurement and, most importantly, nobody was overburdened. Although Homeloans had opted for a comparatively 'big launch', involving seven critical processes which run through the whole organisation, no one section was expected to be completing more than one chart.

These seven critical processes were identified through a Metaplan brainstorming session (where all the ideas are written on pieces of paper and posted round the walls) with a number of operational managers. Careful thought was then given as to which part of each process should be measured: it was decided that each PIC application had to be designed to provide answers to a specific problem, rather than being introduced for the sake of conformity.

Among the processes selected were 'Application Packaging' and 'Application Processing'. Application packaging checks that all incoming action requests contain the full correct documentation: this answers the question, 'is all incoming information being received correctly?' Common reasons for applications not being correctly packaged were identified and the number of instances of each type of non-conformance recorded. These reasons were also weighted to reflect the impact they have on customer service (the degree of 'hassle' they cause): for instance 'MIRAS form missing or incomplete' received a weighted value of 5 whilst 'Checklist/control sheet not enclosed or incomplete' received a weighting of only 1. With the MIRAS form, nothing could be done without further contact with the branch or the customer; a missing or incomplete checklist does not necessarily delay the processing of the application.

Weighting simply means that the score against a certain category is multiplied by the weight attached to it: if there were three instances of an incomplete MIRAS form, this would be multiplied by the weighting factor of 5 and recorded as a score of 15.

Application processing effectively follows the documentation through its next stage at Homeloans, answering the question 'if we have received the application correctly, are we processing it correctly?' This works in very much the same way, with the most common reasons for non-conformance being recorded, logged and weighted. In this case, the omission of a condition from an offer letter is not regarded as particularly serious and is weighted at 1: however, the approval of a case when it falls outside lending criteria is sufficiently damaging to the organisation (and the customer) to merit an 8.

At this stage, TSB feel that it is too early to claim any lasting benefits from PIC. However, the introductory phase does appear to be very successful. Teams involved have taken full ownership of the charts, which are now displayed publicly all around the office. Although Homeloans management have not issued league tables of performance based on the measurement, no Team wants to be seen to be recording the most instances of non-conformance. This is recognised as a common phenomenon when measurement of any kind is introduced into a new environment: the problems improve automatically without the need for any further action. Staff are so surprised by the extent of some of the process problems that they adapt their existing working practice without any management involvement.

The problem with this is that, frequently, such improvement is not sustainable and because the real problems are not being resolved, staff will become demoralised as they see their improvement efforts disappear. Homeloans are prepared for this and, each month, are having brainstorming sessions to identify the problems which have become apparent in the various processes being measured and to allocate responsibility and resource for resolving them. From the managers' point of view, the task is to convince staff that such a measurement exercise is not a flash in the pan but a continuous tool for improvement. Whilst initial results may sometimes be dramatic, the real benefit comes from the sustainable improvements to the process.

CASE STUDY 3: SURFACE MOUNT TECHNOLOGY AT MARS ELECTRONICS

This case study* represents the first Taguchi application at Mars Electronics, which was undertaken with the assistance of Services Ltd. Fundamentally, it is a 'routine' rather than a 'trouble-shooting' case.

Surface Mount Technology

Surface mount components differ from conventional electronic components in that they do not have 'pins' which pass through holes in printed circuit boards. Because of this, the components can be made much smaller and, consequently, the circuit boards can have higher component densities. This leads to smaller circuit boards with greater levels of functionality. Because of these advantages, the current market share of these components has grown dramatically from 12 per cent in 1986 to 30–40 per cent in 1990.

The small size of surface mounted components also has one significant disadvantage, namely that they must be positioned with more precision than conventional components. The normal spacing between the 'pins' of a conventional integrated circuit is 0.1 inch. On a surface mounted integrated circuit the 'leg' spacing is 0.05 inch. This difference of a factor of two is significant when considering the capabilities of high volume component placement machines. It is therefore important to optimise the performance of the placement machines, so that high yields can be reliably achieved.

Mars Electronics and Surface Mount Technology

Mars Electronics is a leading manufacturer of coin validation equipment and has extensive experience of conventional electronic components, together with the associated automated assembly machines. To maintain its market position Mars Electronics invests in innovative technologies, among them surface mount techniques,

* Reprinted by special permission from *Taguchi Methodology within Total Quality*, by Professor Tony Bendell, Graham Wilson and Robert M.G. Millar. Copyright 1990, IFS Ltd, Kempston, Bedford, United Kingdom.

and, at the time of the first experiment, had used surface mounted components for several years. Many products can only be made with this technology because of the number of functions which must be incorporated on small printed circuit boards. The processes involved in surface mount technology include screen printing (for putting down solder paste), placement machines, curing ovens, vapour-phase solder reflow and wave soldering. The effectiveness of the placement machines and the screen printer are dependent on positional accuracies and tolerances; the other processes are not affected by the small size of surface mount components.

Significant engineering effort is usually required to set up a process machine even though it is bought as a standard catalogue item.

Choice of Taguchi Equipment

The Engineering Quality Department at Mars Electronics was, in early 1987, looking for a production process on which to try Taguchi-style optimisation. The purpose was to evaluate the Taguchi method of experimentation and analysis, and to gain sufficient experience so that if it was successful it would be feasible to extend the procedure both to other processes and to product design.

The constraints on which process to choose were many and varied. The process had to have a suitable level of complexity to suit an experimental design of reasonable size: too simple a process would not test the technique; too large a process would result in time-consuming and unwieldy experiments. The process had to be visible within the company so that success could be easily advertised to promote the Taguchi technique. The timing of the trial was also important. The process should be at the commissioning stage, but not so close to the planned completion date that failure would jeopardize the company's performance. This constraint was eventually crucial in deciding which process to experiment on.

A process for surface mount components which consists of a screen printer for solder paste, followed by a 'pick-and-place' machine and an infra-red oven for solder reflow was considered for the trial. It was soon decided that the complete process (known as

SMD2) was too large for experimentation. The screen printer was then selected as the subprocess with most scope for adjustment. A pre-trial, however, showed that variability in the placement machine was causing significant problems, whereas the screen printer appeared to be under control. The 'pick-and-place' machine was therefore deemed to be appropriate for the trial.

A section of printed circuit board with two surface mount integrated circuits on it showed that the 'legs' on the integrated circuits (eleven on each side) did not exactly align with the printed pads on the circuit board. The purpose of the Taguchi experiment was to find control settings on the SMD2 placement machine which would give accurate positioning of the integrated circuits.

One feature of this product and the process is that there are two identical printed circuit boards on one panel, and each board has two integrated circuits (labelled 'AMI' and 'MARS') with nominally identical packaging. The integrated circuits are carried in tubes on the SMD2 machine (tracks on the SMD2 placement machine each hold a tube of components, three tracks for each component type); the placement machine picks up the components with a vacuum nozzle. If it fails to pick it up in three attempts it assumes that a tube is empty and tries another tube. The machine has two sets of jaws ('tweezers') which are used to align and position components on the vaccum nozzle after they have been picked up. The placement of components on to the boards is under numerical control; the SMD2 placement machine has co-ordinates for every component programmed into it.

A measure of 'accuracy of placement' was identified based upon the maximum displacement at any corner of the square integrated circuits.

To allow the experiment to proceed quickly it was decided to photograph each circuit board after the components had been mounted. The time-consuming measurements could be taken at a later time from the photographs.

In the experiment we wished to minimise the inaccuracy of position (y) so that the appropriate optimisation criterion is Taguchi's 'smallest is best'.

Design the Initial Experiment

A number of possible factors affecting the placement of the components were discussed, and attempts made to categorise these as control or noise factors. Six different designs were drawn out and discussed for their practicality with eventually five control and five noise factors being identified, as shown in Figure 10.17, together with the number of levels for each factor.

Figure 10.17   Factors and number of levels

Control factors		Noise factors	
Speed of convergence of jaws	(2)	Board on panel	(2)
Pressure of squeezing jaws A	(3)	Component type	(2)
Pressure of squeezing jaws B	(3)	Track–component type 1	(3)
Placement force	(3)	Track–component type 2	(3)
Tweezer mode	(2)	Time trend	(4)

After consulting a table of common orthogonal arrays, the L^{16} orthogonal array was selected for both the inner array of control factors and the outer array of noise factors; this being the smallest orthogonal array capable of coping with this number of factors and levels without combining factors. The total number of trials required in the experiment was therefore $16 \times 16 = 256$ trials, each combination of control factors being run at each combination of noise factors.

The major disadvantage of the L_{16} design was the number of 'dummy' levels required for this experiment. Where the experiment required only three levels for a factor, the fourth level in the orthogonal array was set equal to the central (nominal) level.

In Figure 10.18 each cell represents a particular combination of control and noise factor levels. In subsequent analysis, each row shows the effect of noise factors on placement accuracy for a given combination of control factors.

The ideal method of conducting the experiment would have been a complete randomisation of all 256 trials, but the time trend noise

Figure 10.18   Complete Parameter Design

			16	15	14	13	12	11	10	9	8	7	6	5	4	3	2	1	Row no.	
			4	4	4	4	3	3	3	3	2	2	2	2	1	1	1	1	F	
		L_{16}	4	3	2	1	4	3	2	1	4	3	2	1	4	3	2	1	G	
		outer array	1	2	3	4	2	1	4	3	3	4	1	2	4	3	2	1	H	Noise
			3	4	1	2	1	2	3	4	2	1	4	3	4	3	2	1	I	factors
			2	1	4	3	3	4	1	2	1	2	3	4	4	3	2	1	J	
			2	2	2	2	1	1	1	1	2	2	2	2	1	1	1	1	F	
			A	M	A	M	A	M	A	M	A	M	A	M	A	M	A	M	G	
			A	B	C	A	B	A	A	C	C	A	A	B	A	C	B	A	H	
			C	A	A	B	A	B	C	A	B	A	A	C	A	C	B	A	I	
Control factors			2	1	4	3	3	4	1	2	1	2	3	4	4	3	2	1	J	

	Row No.	A	B	C	D	E	A	B	C	D	E															Mean	S/N ratio
	1	1	1	1	1	1	C	30	30	30	NW	21	11	13	3	6	8	14	13	20	9	16	8	8	10 9 8	11.06	−21.60
	2	1	2	2	2	2	C	35	35	40	BT															8.75	−20.18
	3	1	3	3	3	3	C	45	45	45	NW															9.31	−20.21
	4	1	4	4	4	4	C	35	35	40	BT															9.19	−20.19
	5	2	1	2	3	4	S	30	35	45	BT															9.00	−20.68
L_{16}	6	2	2	1	4	3	S	35	30	40	NW															9.34	−20.76
inner	7	2	3	4	1	2	S	45	35	30	BT															8.34	−19.17
array	8	2	4	3	2	1	S	35	45	40	NW															9.63	−21.07
	9	3	1	3	4	2	C	30	45	40	BT															11.50	−22.23
	10	3	2	4	3	1	C	35	35	45	NW															9.44	−20.57
	11	3	3	1	2	4	C	45	30	40	BT															10.25	−21.35
	12	3	4	2	1	3	C	35	35	30	NW															11.50	−22.09
	13	4	1	4	2	3	S	30	35	40	NW															8.75	−20.75
	14	4	2	3	1	4	S	35	45	30	BT															8.88	−20.79
	15	4	3	2	4	1	S	45	35	40	NW															8.81	−20.28
	16	4	4	1	3	2	S	35	30	45	BT															8.44	−19.79

factor prohibited this if the experiment was to be completed in a reasonable time. For operational reasons, it was decided to conduct the experiment over two days with 32 trials in each time trend per day. As the speed of convergence of the jaws was very difficult to reset and the tweezer mode difficult to change, it was decided to block the experiment over these variables (see Figure 10.19). Within the block of 16, the tracks were blocked in fours to minimise changes for added convenience.

Conducting the Experiment

Scheduled maintenance of the machine took place in the week prior to the experiment and the photographic equipment was mounted in place. For convenience, the photographic equipment was mounted vertically above a separate table to which the boards were manually transported following component placement. The complete production process required manual transfer of boards at this stage.

Although it had been understood that the components would be sufficiently stable for this transfer to be undertaken satisfactorily, the effect of movement was an uncontrollable noise factor. In running

Figure 10.19   Grouping of Difficult to Change Factors

	Trials	Time trend (J)	Speed of convergence (A)	Tweezer mode (E)
Day 1	1-16	1	C	NW
	17-32	1	C	BT
	33-48	2	C	BT
	49-64	2	C	NW
	65-80	3	S	NW
	81-96	3	S	BT
	97-112	4	S	BT
	113-128	4	S	NW
Day 2	129-144	1	S	NW
	145-160	1	S	BT
	161-176	2	S	BT
	177-192	2	S	NW
	193-208	3	C	NW
	209-224	3	C	BT
	225-240	4	C	BT
	241-256	4	C	NW

the experiment some of the components were found to be loose, and, on rare occasions, fell off the board. Where such movement was identified, the trial was repeated. At first, steady progress was made, but when the tweezer mode was changed to 'both together' for trial 17, the vacuum nozzle experienced difficulty in picking up the component from the track. This was caused by an unexpected interaction which impaired machine operation.

After several adjustments and failures it became evident that the original time schedule would not be adhered to, so that the first morning's 64 trials were abandoned at trial 20. A fresh start was made at trial 65 in the afternoon using narrower and achievable levels for two of the control factors. This was done to maintain the time trend and, as the remainder of the experiment was concluded with only minor hitches, the first 20 trials were repeated and the remaining 44 trials completed in the morning of the third day.

Several important points concerning the conduct of the experiment were raised during these three days: all equipment and machinery to be used should be fully overhauled prior to the experiment, time should be allowed for the experiment to over-run, and statistical expertise should be available while conducting the experiment, so that if changes have to be effected, they will have minimal effect on the randomisation.

Initial Analysis

The aim was to identify the control factor levels which minimise the mean displacement and the relative variation in displacement over various combinations of noise factor levels. Of course, the optimum combination of control factor levels for the mean response may be different from that for the relative variation signal to noise.

Using the standard Taguchi approach, the mean response for each row i of the inner array was calculated by the formula:

$$y_i = \frac{1}{n}\sum_{j=1}^{n} y_{ij}$$

and the signal-to-noise ratio by:

$$z_i = -10 \log \left(\frac{1}{n}\sum_{j=1}^{n} y_{ij}^2 \right)$$

where y_{ij} represents the response for row i in the inner array and column j of the outer array. (See Bendell, Disney and Pridmore, 1989).

Figure 10.20 shows the graphs for the signal-to-noise and mean response of each of the control factors, in each case averaging out the respective statistic for each level of the factor. It is apparent from the graphs that, in this case, control factor levels for minimising mean inaccuracy of placement and maximising the signal-to-noise ratio are identical. Within the range of control factor levels considered, the slower speed of the convergence of the jaws and the higher the placement force the better. However, for the pressure of squeezing the behaviours of the two jaws differ with 45 psi being superior for jaw A and 35psi for jaw B. The 'both together' tweezer mode is

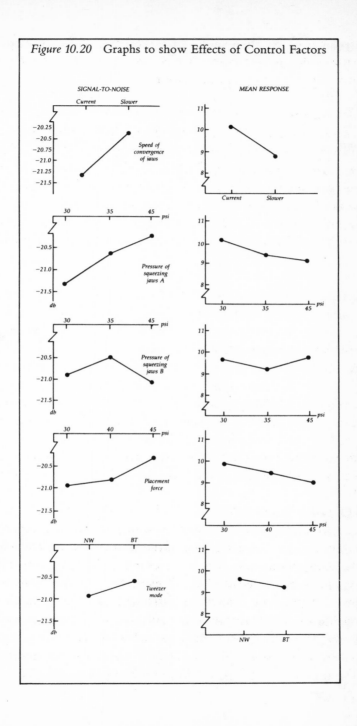

Figure 10.20 Graphs to show Effects of Control Factors

better than 'narrow then wide'. The optimum control factor level controls are shown in Figure 10.21.

Figure 10.21 Optimum control factor levels as determined graphically

Control factors	Optimum level
Speed of convergence of jaws	Slower
Pressure of squeezing jaws A	45 psi
Pressure of squeezing jaws B	35 psi
Placement force	45 psi
Tweezer mode	BT

Analysis of Variance (ANOVA) techniques were applied to test the significance of the differences. This was important in view of the nature of the technology involved; it would, for example, be undesirable to run the equipment at extreme pressure values for only a very slight improvement in quality. ANOVA was therefore applied to the signal–to–noise ratios and the mean responses.

In this initial analysis, none of the factors was shown to have a significant effect at the 5 per cent level on the signal–to–noise ratio, but speed of the convergence of the jaws (Factor A) was shown to have a significant effect on the mean response at the 2.5 per cent level.

More Detailed Analysis

The results of this initial ANOVA were disappointing and the lack of significance of these global results prompted an investigation into the different components on each panel. The orthogonality of the experimental design allowed the data to be split into four subsets, and the exploratory data analysis was undertaken on each subset. By considering the mean response for each subset, in conjunction with the photographs of all trials, the best and worst components on each panel were determined; the 'MARS' component on board 2 was clearly the best and the 'AMI' component on board 2 the worst.

For the 'MARS' component on board 2, the speed of convergence of the jaws is not only more significant in determining the mean response but is also significant for the signal–to–noise ratio. It is also noteworthy that for this best component/board combination, the optimum pressure of squeezing for jaws A and B is in both cases 35 psi, in contrast to the global results.

For the worst component, which is the 'AMI' component on board 2, it is also interesting that no control factors were significant. Because of the extremity of this case, there was some reason to believe that a programming error had taken place in the calibration of the robotic arm for this component.

Although the significance of the speed of convergence of the jaws is important, the insignificance of the other control factors together with the differing results for the various component/board combinations suggests that much of the variability in the response is accounted for by the noise factors. Accordingly, it was of interest to investigate whether any particular noise factor was contributing excessively to this variation. (See Figure 10.22.)

Conclusion

The movement to surface mount technology is both largely unavoidable and difficult to implement. The pilot experiment described here, which was the first Taguchi experiment at Mars Electronics, provided valuable information in helping to understand the implementation of the technology. From this pilot experiment, considerable experience has been gained as to the application of Taguchi methods to this technology. The experiment was achieved with 256 trials (lasting only three days), compared with up to 15,552 trials (circa 120 days) that would have been required with traditional full factorial designs.

As with all good experiments, the results were not entirely as expected. The control settings for most parameters did not show large effects. One major gain was that the setting for 'speed of convergence' (slower is better) was not anticipated, but with hindsight was easily explained and led to a significant improvement in the process capability.

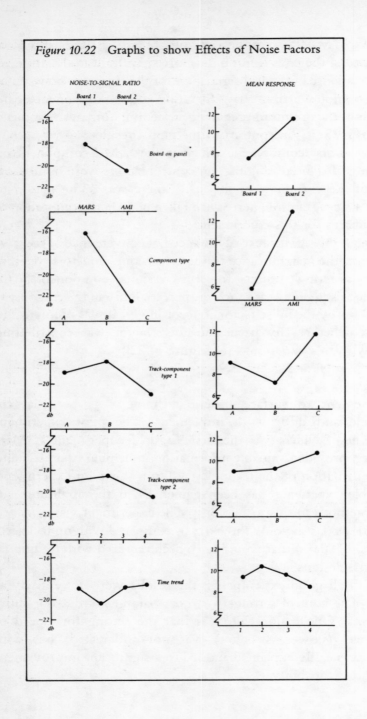

Figure 10.22 Graphs to show Effects of Noise Factors

The analysis of the noise factors did yield some surprises. The fact that no time trend was observed was unexpected, as was the fact that the tracks from which the components were taken did not affect accuracy. These results simplified later experiments.

The very strong effect of 'component type' and 'board' on placement accuracy gave rise to a lot of speculation and theorising about the cause of the effect. Further examination of the photographs finally resolved the question. The chosen measure of accuracy (worst displacement) had an implicit assumption that the components suffered a displacement in a random direction From the optimum position. In practice, the displacement for the component/board combinations with low 'accuracy' was consistently in one direction. The mean displacement was some three times larger than the scatter in the displacements. The cause was established as incorrect programming of the placement machine; some of the components had positional offsets programmed in. This enabled the introduction of substantial improvements in the programming of the placement arm.

The Taguchi trial yielded optimum control settings for the placement machine, as well as revealing an error in programming. The procedure for programming was subsequently changed to prevent the error from recurring. Follow-up experiments could be much smaller than the original trial because two of the noise factors ('time' and 'track number') are known to have no effect.

CASE STUDY 4: APPLICATION OF TAGUCHI METHODOLOGY TO FOOD PACKAGING

Problem Setting
This case study* concerns a specialist food producer who had developed a high volume line, but which after a substantial amount

---

* Reprinted by special permission from *Taguchi Methodology within Total Quality*, by Professor Tony Bendell, Graham Wilson and Roger M.G. Millar. Copyright 1990, IFS Ltd, Kempston, Bedford, United Kingdom.

of time in commissioning was still not able to produce its major intended product. A less important product could be produced. The line was a second generation development to produce a product in high demand. Following company policy it was composed mainly of two sub-assemblies from different manufacturers, plus an internally developed transfer table. The line had cost in excess of £2 million.

In consequence, this case concerns the use of Taguchi methodology for a major *problem solving* exercise rather than for routine process optimisation.

Brainstorming

Because of the criticality of the application, this took several weeks. Four main responses were identified. These were:

- Only capable of evaluation by testing
- 'Indicators' of field performance
- One 'biggest is best', one 'smallest is best'
- Expected to have different optima and not to be correlated (see Figure 10.23)

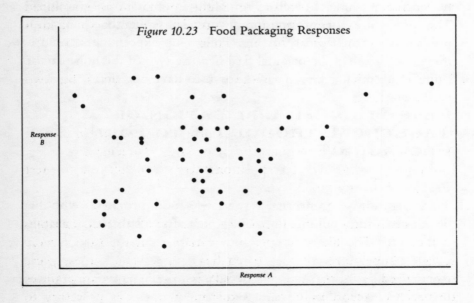

Figure 10.23 Food Packaging Responses

The brainstorming team worked very effectively together with a high level of motivation. An illustration of this was that the team members agreed amongst themselves that they would take charge personally of shifts during the experiment.

Control and Noise Factors

Given the complexity of the process, there were a large number of possible control variables. Those finally selected included:

- Materials
  - Two packaging materials
  - Content material
- Process
  - Machine speed
  - Tension in packaging laminate rate, registration
  - Temperatures, pressures, coating thickness of heated jaws
  - Line configuration (presence of cooling jaw)
  - Presence or absence of guards (absence was used to check for the effects of excessive heat contamination)
- Human
  - Test operator (whilst this could have been included as a noise factor, it was made a control factor to limit the size of the experiment)

There was initial scepticism about potential noise factors, but two were identified:

- Lanes
  - There were six lanes producing product in parallel
- Test
  - Both responses were pressure characteristics

Positions
  and five test positions were available on the test equipment.

An interesting point concerned the selection of 'correct' variables to measure. The likely temperature variables of importance were surface temperatures of the coated heated jaws (since these were experienced by the packaging material), not the set jaw temperatures themselves. Accordingly, prior experimentation was necessary to establish the jaw temperature settings to obtain given surface temperatures for given coating thicknesses.

Experimental Design

Several attempts were made at the experimental design, some in parallel, in order to identify their relative advantages and disadvantages. The selection of control variables was ultimately achieved by restricting choice to all 'easy to change' variables, i.e. those that required no retooling and could be changed in a day.

The final experimental design selected was an L_{54} orthogonal array for the control factors crossed by a 6×5 (6 lanes $\times$ 5 test positions) full factorial for the noise factors. The experiment was scheduled to take six to seven days in two 12 hour shifts per day. The production window available for experimentation was just eight days.

Various physical inertias were inherent in the production equipment, and thus the experiment, which made both its conduct and the use of randomisation difficult. In particular, the following variables were difficult or time-consuming to change or to reset:

- Temperature
- Content
- Guards
- Packaging materials
- Machine speed
- Coating of jaws

Thus, in conducting the experiment a hierarchy of blocks was necessary in order to accommodate the hard-to-change variables, with the less hard-to-change variables sequentially blocked within harder-to-change ones. Randomisation was thus of the order of blocks and of sub-blocks within blocks etc. The L_{54} orthogonal array (Figure 10.24) accommodates this well since the variables in columns 1–8 are all blocked.

Figure 10.24 The L₅₄ Orthogonal Array

$$L_{54} \ (2^1 \times 3^{26})$$

Trial no.	1	2	3	4	5	6	7	8	9	10	11	12	13	14	15	16	17	18	19	20	21	22	23	24	25	26
1	1	1	1	1	1	1	1	1	1	1	1	1	1	1	1	1	1	1	1	1	1	1	1	1	1	1
2	1	1	1	1	1	1	1	1	2	2	2	2	2	2	2	2	2	2	2	2	2	2	2	2	2	2
3	1	1	1	1	1	1	1	1	3	3	3	3	3	3	3	3	3	3	3	3	3	3	3	3	3	3
4	1	1	2	2	2	2	2	2	1	1	1	1	1	1	2	3	2	3	2	3	2	3	2	3	2	3
5	1	1	2	2	2	2	2	2	2	2	2	2	2	2	3	1	3	1	3	1	3	1	3	1	3	1
6	1	1	2	2	2	2	2	2	3	3	3	3	3	3	1	2	1	2	1	2	1	2	1	2	1	2
7	1	1	3	3	3	3	3	3	1	1	1	1	1	1	3	2	3	2	3	2	3	2	3	2	3	2
8	1	1	3	3	3	3	3	3	2	2	2	2	2	2	1	3	1	3	1	3	1	3	1	3	1	3
9	1	1	3	3	3	3	3	3	3	3	3	3	3	3	2	1	2	1	2	1	2	1	2	1	2	1
10	1	2	1	1	2	2	3	3	1	1	2	2	3	3	1	1	1	1	2	3	2	3	3	2	3	2
11	1	2	1	1	2	2	3	3	2	2	3	3	1	1	2	2	2	2	3	1	3	1	1	3	1	3
12	1	2	1	1	2	2	3	3	3	3	1	1	2	2	3	3	3	3	1	2	1	2	2	1	2	1
13	1	2	2	2	3	3	1	1	1	1	2	2	3	3	2	3	2	3	3	2	3	2	1	1	1	1
14	1	2	2	2	3	3	1	1	2	2	3	3	1	1	3	1	3	1	1	3	1	3	2	2	2	2
15	1	2	2	2	3	3	1	1	3	3	1	1	2	2	1	2	1	2	2	1	2	1	3	3	3	3
16	1	2	3	3	1	1	2	2	1	1	2	2	3	3	3	2	3	2	1	1	1	1	2	3	2	3
17	1	2	3	3	1	1	2	2	2	2	3	3	1	1	1	3	1	3	2	2	2	2	3	1	3	1
18	1	2	3	3	1	1	2	2	3	3	1	1	2	2	2	1	2	1	3	3	3	3	1	2	1	2
19	1	3	1	2	1	3	2	3	1	2	1	3	2	3	1	1	2	3	1	1	3	2	2	3	3	2
20	1	3	1	2	1	3	2	3	2	3	2	1	3	1	2	2	3	1	2	2	1	3	3	1	1	3
21	1	3	1	2	1	3	2	3	3	1	3	2	1	2	3	3	1	2	3	3	2	1	1	2	2	1
22	1	3	2	3	2	1	3	1	1	2	1	3	2	3	2	3	3	2	2	1	1	1	3	2	1	1
23	1	3	2	3	2	1	3	1	2	3	2	1	3	1	3	1	1	3	3	1	2	2	1	3	2	2
24	1	3	2	3	2	1	3	1	3	1	3	2	1	2	1	2	2	1	1	2	3	3	2	1	3	3
25	1	3	3	1	3	2	1	2	1	2	1	3	2	3	3	2	1	1	3	2	2	3	1	1	2	3
26	1	3	3	1	3	2	1	2	2	3	2	1	3	1	1	3	2	2	1	3	3	1	2	2	3	1
27	1	3	3	1	3	2	1	2	3	1	3	2	1	2	2	1	3	3	2	1	1	2	3	3	1	2
28	2	1	1	3	3	2	2	1	1	3	3	2	2	1	1	1	3	2	3	2	2	3	2	3	1	1
29	2	1	1	3	3	2	2	1	2	1	1	3	3	2	2	2	1	3	1	3	3	1	3	1	2	2
30	2	1	1	3	3	2	2	1	3	2	2	1	1	3	3	3	2	1	2	1	1	2	1	2	3	3
31	2	1	2	1	1	3	3	2	1	3	3	2	2	1	2	3	1	1	1	1	3	2	3	2	2	3
32	2	1	2	1	1	3	3	2	2	1	1	3	3	2	3	1	2	2	2	2	1	3	1	3	3	1
33	2	1	2	1	1	3	3	2	3	2	2	1	1	3	1	2	3	3	3	3	2	1	2	1	1	2
34	2	1	3	2	2	1	1	3	1	3	3	2	2	1	3	2	2	3	2	3	1	1	1	1	3	2
35	2	1	3	2	2	1	1	3	2	1	1	3	3	2	1	3	3	1	3	1	2	2	2	2	1	3
36	2	1	3	2	2	1	1	3	3	2	2	1	1	3	2	1	1	2	1	2	3	3	3	3	2	1
37	2	2	1	2	3	1	3	2	1	2	3	1	3	2	1	1	2	3	3	2	1	1	3	2	2	3
38	2	2	1	2	3	1	3	2	2	3	1	2	1	3	2	2	3	1	1	3	2	2	1	3	3	1
39	2	2	1	2	3	1	3	2	3	1	2	3	2	1	3	3	1	2	2	1	3	3	2	1	1	2
40	2	2	2	3	1	2	1	3	1	2	3	1	3	2	2	3	3	2	1	1	2	3	1	1	3	2
41	2	2	2	3	1	2	1	3	2	3	1	2	1	3	3	1	1	3	2	2	3	1	2	2	1	3
42	2	2	2	3	1	2	1	3	3	1	2	3	2	1	1	2	2	1	3	3	1	2	3	3	2	1
43	2	2	3	1	2	3	2	1	1	2	3	1	3	2	3	2	1	1	2	3	3	2	2	3	1	1
44	2	2	3	1	2	3	2	1	2	3	1	2	1	3	1	3	2	2	3	1	1	3	3	1	2	2
45	2	2	3	1	2	3	2	1	3	1	2	3	2	1	2	1	3	3	1	2	2	1	1	2	3	3
46	2	3	1	3	2	3	1	2	1	3	2	3	1	2	1	1	3	2	2	3	3	2	1	1	2	3
47	2	3	1	3	2	3	1	2	2	1	3	1	2	3	2	2	1	3	3	1	1	3	2	2	3	1
48	2	3	1	3	2	3	1	2	3	2	1	2	3	1	3	3	2	1	1	2	2	1	3	3	1	2
49	2	3	2	1	3	1	2	3	1	3	2	3	1	2	2	3	1	1	3	2	1	1	2	3	3	2
50	2	3	2	1	3	1	2	3	2	1	3	1	2	3	3	1	2	2	1	3	2	2	3	1	1	3
51	2	3	2	1	3	1	2	3	3	2	1	2	3	1	1	2	3	3	2	1	3	3	1	2	2	1
52	2	3	3	2	1	2	3	1	1	3	2	3	1	2	3	2	2	3	1	1	2	3	3	2	1	1
53	2	3	3	2	1	2	3	1	2	1	3	1	2	3	1	3	3	1	2	2	3	1	1	3	2	2
54	2	3	3	2	1	2	3	1	3	2	1	2	3	1	2	1	1	2	3	3	1	2	2	1	3	3

Column 1 (the only two level variable) contains two blocks of 27, which each divide into three blocks of nine in column 2. Columns 3–8 divide these sub-blocks further into three sub-sub-blocks of three.

Preparation and Conduct of Experiment

As preparation for the experiment:

- The brainstorming team took charge of the shifts.
- Fitters and operators were briefed.
- Strict protocols were established for the trials and the experimental regime.
- Labelling systems and arrangements for the protection of products were agreed and implemented. Multiple automated labelling was agreed.
- One week's rest was planned for recovery and product 'settling' after manufacture and before testing.
- Arrangements were made to have one of the statistical experts on site at all the critical change-overs, and on telephone call at all other times in the experiment.
- Some preparatory experimentation took place, but in retrospect (as usual) perhaps not enough.
- It was planned to produce one box of product (circa 100 packs) per 54 combinations × 6 lanes.

In conducting the experiment, the following circumstances were experienced:

- High level of staff motivation.
- The need to redefine (narrow the range of) one factor level at the start in order to facilitate experimentation and production.
- Major change-overs were found to be slow. This was due to the need to get the line back 'in control' (not statistical control), following each major change-over. In consequence, there was a danger of running out of materials. Thus it was necessary to arrange for additional materials to be brought in at short notice, and in case these did not arrive in time plans were put in place to find the least damaging way of sequentially sacrificing the agreed randomised order. In the event, the additional materials arrived just in time, so that this was unnecessary.

Gains

In common with all such experimentation, perhaps in a qualitative sense a third of the gain from the experiment came from the constructive activity in brainstorming, a third from the trials (as particular trials yielded surprises) and a third from the results of the analysis. The optimum settings identified by the analysis were a surprise, and the confirmatory experiment yielded results even better than predicted.

As is to be expected, the experiment yielded both positive and negative information. Negative results are extremely useful in allowing the elimination of the majority of the potential control factors as not seriously affecting the product. On the positive side, the following variables were identified as statistically significant:

- Response A – Machine speed
  - Content
  - One packaging material
  - One temperature
  - One coating
- Response B – Cooling jaw
  - Other packaging material
  - Test operator
  - Same temperature

Since there is only one common significant control factor (a temperature), the various control factors could largely be used to adjust the two responses to their predicted optimum separately. Thus, only little trade-off between the two separate optima was necessary; this is unusual and was a great windfall.

Operator Effect

There was initial scepticism as to why for Response B there appeared to be significant differences between test operators. Consequently, the operators were observed, and a subjective element in the test procedure identified which accounted for the effect seen. The test specification was improved and the problem did not recur.

Implication

The major implication was that the process moved immediately into a full production state. Ironically, but not unforeseen, this prevented the continuation of experimentation to obtain further, but more minor, gains by 'zooming-in' on optimum settings.

The other main implication was that there immediately developed much in-house interest in the methodology. The brainstorming team members found themselves as 'local gurus' and were soon out of their depth. Extensive training (given the size of the company) has now taken place via two in-house four-day courses, and these have been backed up where necessary by on-site clinics. The company is now using the methods in diverse applications, and interest has spread to other companies in the group.

CASE STUDY 5: IBM, HAVANT

The Havant manufacturing plant of IBM are embarking on a journey to:

1. understand the Taguchi methodology
2. understand its relevance to their business
3. through pilot studies evaluate its potential for success
4. understand its place vis à vis standard Design of Experiment methodologies
5. understand its relevance to improving Quality at source.

The following application to an adhesion process represents part of the journey; namely an evaluation of its potential, through a pilot study on a particular problem in the plant.

Problem Background

A new file product is under development in the plant. A problem was experienced with the actuator assembly. One of the parts making up the actuator assembly is called the core rail assembly (produced by external vendors). This assembly comprises two elements; namely the core (made of mild steel and coated with electroless Nickel plating), and rails (made of ceramic which is very smooth and chemically inert). The assembly of these parts is through joining via a suitable adhesive. Unfortunately as much as a 50 per cent failure rate of the bond of core to rail was being experienced in the early stages of file development. An immediate screen was instituted to protect the line from using suspect assemblies. At the same time it was decided that the adhesive type originally specified was suspect, and that an alternative, together with a suitable adhesion process for implementation at the vendors, should be sought. The laboratory identified what they believed, and justified through experimentation, would be a suitable adhesive type. They sought help on the development of a suitable process.

This seemed a good opportunity to apply Taguchi methods and test their relevance.

The Approach Taken

One of the elements of the Taguchi approach is the importance of structure to examination of a problem. The structure used by IBM, Havant can be summarised as follows:

1. Problem definition
2. Identification of the objectives of the experiment
3. Identifying what to measure and how
4. Process definition
5. Establishment of causal factors
6. Definition of control/noise factors and interactions
7. Definition of levels/settings for all factors
8. Experimental design and selection of orthogonal array
9. Definition of experimental material requirement – how many samples?
10. Plan experimental sequence – recording sheets
11. Perform experiment
12. Analyse results
13. Determine 'best' conditions to satisfy objective
14. Prediction at 'best' conditions and evaluating confidence in result
15. Checking by confirmation trial
16. Possible further experimentation in 'best' zone

Application of the Approach

1. *Problem Definition*
The current bond of core to rail does not meet the strength requirement of 2 KNewtons (a Newton is an SI unit of force).

2. *The objectives*
   1) To define a process to enable the joint of core to the rail to withstand a force of at least 2 KNewtons.
   2) Ensure that any excess adhesive can be easily cleaned by solvent cleaning.

3. *Measurement*
   1) Establish the load required to break the joint when applied axially at the end of the rail.
   2) Excess adhesive to a visual standard.

4/5. *Process definition/causal factors*
This is a most crucial step. Failure to comply with it thoroughly will almost certainly lead to failure of the objectives.

Through a 'brainstorm' with the relevant people involved with the process the Process Flow shown in Figure 10.25 was established. At the same time, and by making reference to the process stages, a possible 'critical' set of process parameters were identified. These are shown on the figure.

6/7. *Control/Noise factors and their settings*
Again these were established through the 'brainstorm' meeting. The final combination was not achieved through a one-off meeting. This was especially true of the settings to be used where the objective is to establish the 'robustness' of a particular parameter.

The final combinations are shown in Figure 10.26.

There was one noise factor associated with the position of the rail in the core. Since this was a feature of the part, and therefore unchangeable, any defined process must be able to satisfy the objectives regardless of the core position.

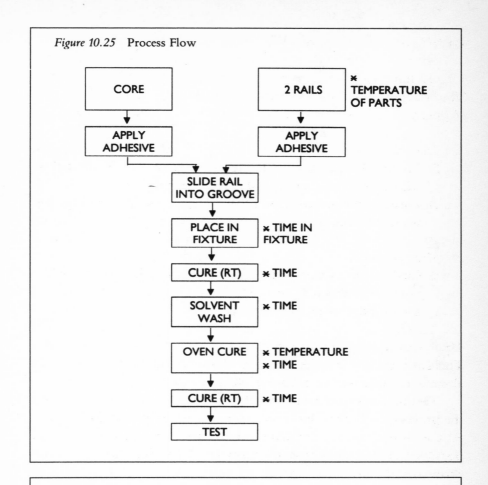

Figure 10.25   Process Flow

Figure 10.26   Control Factors – Levels

LABEL	FACTOR	LEVEL	
		1	2
A	TEMPERATURE PARTS	20 C	50 C
B	TIME IN FIXTURE	5 m	15 m
C	TIME TO CURE	30 m	120 m
D	TIME IN OVEN	30 m	60 m
E	TIME IN SOLVENT	5 m	20 m
F	TIME CURE POST OVEN	4 h	12 h
G	TEMP OVEN CURE	20 C	100 C

8. *Experimental Design – Orthogonal Array*

The size of the array chosen was determined through an examination of the number of degrees of freedom associated with the control factors. An L_{12} array was selected.

9. *Sample sizes/Replications*

To get a realistic assessment of sample size requires two parameters to be known with a reasonable level of accuracy. These are the standard deviation of the response measurement, together with some estimate of the difference between the responses achieved at the two factor levels, which would be significant. Due to the nature of the data already available (i.e. restricted purely to a knowledge that 50 per cent were failing at around 2 KNewtons) an estimate was made for both these parameters based on 'best knowledge'.

The result of this was a need for around 15 results at each of the two levels, i.e. 30 results in total.

One replication of the L_{12} design would produce 24 results in total, due to the two rails present in a single core. It was decided to replicate the whole experiment, to allow for any inaccuracies in the estimates made on standard deviation and significant difference.

Hence there would be 48 results in total, giving 24 results at each factor level.

10/11. *Plan experimental sequence/recording sheets/experiment*

The L_{12} design was converted into a meaningful experiment statement using the control factor labels already noted, and the appropriate level information. The whole experimental sequence was randomised, using different sequences for the two replications. The experiment was conducted according to the plan.

12. *Analysis*

The fact that we have a noise array with replications means that as well as analysis based purely on the raw data, we can also consider the Taguchi signal-to-noise characteristic. For our study, the response measure is a Largest is Best measure, which converts to a signal to noise (S/N) statement of:

$$S/N = -10 \log \left(\frac{1}{n} \sum_{i=y}^{n} \frac{1}{iy^2} \right)$$

The response graphs are shown in Figure 10.27.

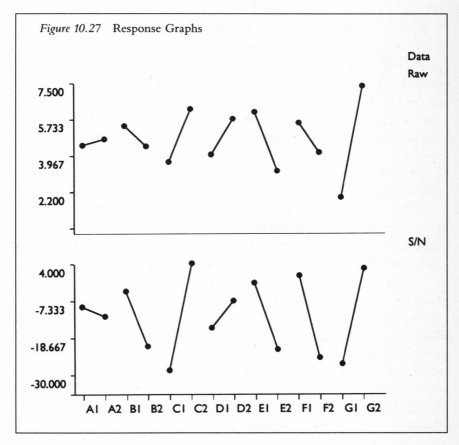

Figure 10.27   Response Graphs

Significant Factors

i) Examination of the response graphs and an ANOVA analysis for raw data shows a more significant difference between the mean levels for factors C,D,E,F,G.

ii) The S/N response graphs follow the indicators noted above for the means, except that factor B suggests a significant effect.

13. 'Best' Conditions

Examination of the significant factors and the level average table shows that the following factor combinations should provide the 'best' mean conditions for the adhesion process.

C   at level 2
D   at level 2
E   at level 1
F   at level 1
G   at level 2

In addition, although having little impact on the mean level,

B   at level 1

is possibly desirable for reduction in variation. The remaining factor A, having no impact on either mean level or S/N can be chosen by other criteria, i.e. cost, speed etc. Since it is easier/cheaper to maintain parts at level 1 (20°C) A was set at level 1.

14. Prediction and Confidence

The predicted strength level if the process were to run under the above conditions (including only the significant factors) is obtained as 11.327 KNewtons. A 90 per cent confidence bound for the predicted value can also be established as 9.724 to 12.93 KNewtons.

15. Confirmation Trial

As final confirmation of the 'best' conditions noted above, a confirmation run on six cores (12 rails) was performed. These conditions were as already noted with the exception of factor B, which was run under level 2 rather than the level 1 suggested by the signal-to-noise analysis, due to a conviction by the process owner that this level would be 'better in production'. Note that this factor had no impact on mean strength. Hence the confirmation conditions were:

A   Parts temperature 20 C
B   Fixture time 15 m
C   Cure time 120 m
D   Oven time 60 m
E   Solvent time 5 m
F   Cure time 4 h
G   Oven temperature 100°C

The confirmation trial data can be summarised as having a mean level of 9.33 KNewtons. The smallest observation in the set of 12 results was 7.64 KNewtons. The distribution shows an insignificant probability of failing against 2 KNewtons. At this stage it really seems that a 'best process' has been achieved.

However, the observed mean is just outside the predicted confidence bound, and this caused some concern in the laboratory. Apparently due to the urgency of needing to define a process, the confirmation experiment had not been performed under quite the same conditions as the original experiment. The conditions for confirmation were potentially corrupted by a failure of the air conditioning system. This caused the environmental conditions to change from the usual 21°C with 64 per cent RH to 25°C with 77 per cent RH. These damp conditions were deemed to be unsuitable for optimum performance of the adhesive. A re-run of the confirmation trial was conducted under normal conditions (with the air conditioning fixed). This resulted in a process mean level of 11.41 KNewtons and a smallest value of 8.90 KNewtons, offering a significant area of safety above the specification need.

Whilst the initial confirmation run would have been accepted in most circumstances, the re-run, however, gave another 'noise' factor, humidity, and showed that the 'best' process was 'robust' to a fairly severe change in this. This knowledge was very useful in the implementation of the process as a vendor process.

16. *Implementation*
The process developed above was implemented in the two vendors supplying core rail assemblies. The results confirmed the adoption of

the 'best' process. It is most likely that some more work could be performed on the vendor process, to understand whether other factors are at play in transferring the laboratory process to the vendor. It was not considered essential to do this in view of the relatively small benefit which would be obtained. This process has now become 'business as usual'.

Benefits of the Experiment

1. The complete experiment, from problem identification through to recommended process, took two weeks.
2. This was reckoned to be a 10 week reduction in what would have been the case through standard approaches.
3. The reduction in time resulted in a saving in parts cost alone of $132,000 over this period.
4. At the last count, 1,200 assemblies had been received into the plant, since the process change, with not one failure.
5. QA laboratory checking had been reduced from 1 in 3 to around 1 in 20, with intent to discontinue totally.
6. The project was submitted to plant management as QA 'best project' in the Process Quality Improvement Activity.

Lessons Learned at IBM, Havant

1. The experiment was a success. The Taguchi approach was readily understood and accepted by the people involved in the experiment. This fact helped significantly in the acceptance of the experiment plan, and was certainly a contributor to the success of the experiment.
2. Experimentation is not easy! There are no quick routes to success.
3. Management commitment is essential. They control the resource needed. i.e. people, materials, process, time.
4. A structured approach is essential. There is a need to be sure of the problem, the objectives and the measurement.
5. A team approach is needed. All involved must feel committed and understand the experiment purpose, to ensure that plans are carried through to practice.

6. The 'brainstorm' is probably the most crucial step. If the wrong experimental space is defined, no amount of statistical theory will recover this.
7. Sample size will always be a limiting factor in experimental scope. A small scale experiment has a better chance of success due to the real difficulties of exercising 'control to plan' over a long period.
8. The confirmation trial is an essential feature. It allows a second look at the conclusions before a change to the process is made.

11. Quality Awards

11.1 INTRODUCTION

With the increase in awareness of the role that quality can play within an organisation, there has been a similar increase in quality awards. These can be seen as raising staff awareness of quality issues. The problem with awards is that they can focus effort towards achieving the award rather than the award reflecting a mark of achievement for the company and the Total Quality programme.

Some companies recognise various stages to quality improvement. One such hierarchy is:

Stage 1	BS 5750/ISO 9000
Stage 2	Ford Q1
Stage 3	European Space Agency

Too many manufacturers see achieving BS 5750 as achieving the set 'goal'. When the certificate is safely on the wall all improvement activity ceases and rather than the company capitalising on the achievement, the system stagnates. The adage that BS 5750 does not stop you losing money but enables you to lose it more systematically, is still true.

WHAT ARE QUALITY AWARDS?

They can be benchmarks for quality; AQAP, Ford Q1, BS 5750, or annual awards given to companies for outstanding achievement. All represent 'marks of excellence' to be achieved. Public awards include the Deming Prize, BQA award, the Baldrige award and the latest on the scene, The European Quality Award. To prepare for third party assessments usually involves the company in a costly and painstaking journey. Not only does presentation of the company's case have to be made but the company structure and operations have to be totally re-evaluated in the light of the award requirements. It is at this stage that senior management can become more fully aware of the deficiencies in their company's quality and quality improvement programme.

In-company awards can be subdivided into two types; for suppliers, and for members of the workforce or departments. Many companies recognise the benefit of increasing their own quality profile and so make annual presentations to these groups. Raising the profile of such awards by making them prestigious, increases competition and quality. Such schemes exist within Texas Instruments, ICL, IBM, Ford and GEC Plessey Telecommunications.

11.2 DEMING PRIZES

The first Deming Prize was awarded in September 1951 in Osaka. The Deming Prize is for an individual and/or group of individuals who have contributed to the development and dissemination of Statistical Quality Control (SQC). There are several different categories of the Deming Application Prize but it is primarily an award given to a company which has performed exceptionally in the field of Statistical Quality Control. These are considered to be the highest awards relating to SQC in Japan.

To demonstrate performance against the Deming Application prize criteria, the following checklist taken from Ishikawa (1985) can be used:

1. *Policy and objectives*

- Policy with regard to management, quality, and quality control
- Methods in determining policy and objectives

- Appropriateness and consistency of the contents of objectives
- Utilisation of statistical methods
- Dissemination and permeation of objectives
- Checking objectives and their implementation
- Relationships with long-range and short-range plans

2. *Organisation and its operation*

- A clear-cut line of responsibilities
- Appropriateness of delegation of power
- Co-operation between divisions
- Activities of committees
- Utilisation of the staff
- Utilisation of QC circle (small-group) activities
- Quality control audit

3. *Education and its dissemination*

- Education plan and actual accomplishment
- Consciousness about quality and control, understanding of quality control
- Education concerning statistical concepts and methods, and degree of permeation
- Ability to understand the effects
- Education for subcontractors and outside organisations
- QC circle (small-group) activities
- Suggestion system

4. *Assembling and disseminating information and its utilisation*

- Assembling outside information
- Disseminating information between divisions
- Speed in disseminating information (use of computer)
- (Statistical) analysis of information and its utilisation

5. *Analysis*

- Selection of important problems and themes
- Appropriateness of the analytical method
- Utilisation of statistical methods
- Tying in with own engineering technology
- Quality analysis, process analysis
- Utilisation of results of analysis
- Positiveness of suggestions for improvement

6. *Standardisation*

- System of standards
- Methods of establishing, revising, and withdrawing standards
- Actual records in establishing, revising, and withdrawing standards
- Contents of standards
- Utilisation of statistical method
- Accumulation of technology
- Utilisation of standards

7. *Control*

- Control systems for quality and in related areas such as cost and quantity
- Control points, and control items
- Utilisation of statistical methods such as the control chart, and general acceptance of the statistical way of thinking
- Contributions of QC circle (small-group) activities
- Actual conditions of control activities
- Actual conditions of control systems

8. *Quality Assurance*

- Procedures for new product development

- Quality development (breakdown of quality function) and its analysis, reliability and design review
- Safety and product liability prevention
- Process control and improvement
- Process capabilities
- Measurement and inspection
- Control of facilities/equipment, subcontracting, purchasing, services, etc.
- Quality assurance system and its audit
- Utilisation of statistical methods
- Evaluation and audit of quality
- Practical conditions of quality assurance

9. *Effects*

- Measuring effects
- Visible effects, such as quality, serviceability, date of delivery, cost, profit, safety, environment, etc.
- Invisible effects
- Compatibility between prediction of effects and actual records

10. *Future plans*

- Understanding of the present conditions, and concreteness
- Policies adopted to solve shortcomings
- Plans of promotion for the future
- Relations with the company's long-range plans

11.3 MALCOLM BALDRIGE NATIONAL QUALITY AWARD

The Malcolm Baldrige National Quality Award was established in 1987 to stimulate American companies to improve quality, recognise achievements, establish guidelines of self-evaluation, and make available information from successful organisations. Criticism of the award is that the emphasis is on participatory management and assumes that other management approaches would not work. The 1991 Baldrige criteria and the relative weights given to each factor and subfactor are shown below. These are taken from a document produced by D.O.D. Reliability Analysis Centre 1990.

The points indicate the relative importance given to each subfactor and are a maximum number that can be scored towards the final assessment score:

Factor	Subfactor	Points
Leadership		
	Senior Executive Leadership	40
	Quality Values	15
	Management for Quality	25
	Public Responsibility	20
Information and Analysis	Scope & Analysis of Quality Data and Information	20
	Competitive Comparisons and Benchmarks	30
	Analysis of Quality Data	20
Strategic Quality Planning	Strategic Quality Planning Process	35
	Quality Goal and Plans	25
Human Resource Utilisation	Human Resource Management	20
	Employee Involvement	40
	Quality Education and Training	40
	Employee Recognition & Performance Measurement	25
	Employee Well-Being and Morale	25
Quality Assurance	Design & Introduction of Quality Products & Services	35
	Process Quality Control	20
	Continuous Improvement of Processes	20
	Quality Assessment	15
	Documentation	10
	Business Process & Support Service Quality	20
	Supplier Quality	20
Quality Results	Product & Service Quality Results	90
	Business Process, Operational, & Support Service Quality Results	50
	Supplier Quality Results	40

Customer Satisfaction

Determining Customer Requirements and Expectations	30
Customer Relationship Management	50
Customer Service Standards	20
Commitment to Customers	15
Complaint Resolution for Quality Improvement	25
Determining Customer Satisfaction	20
Customer Satisfaction Results	70
Customer Satisfaction Comparison	70

11.4 BRITISH QUALITY AWARDS

The British Quality Award Scheme was introduced to encourage total quality improvements in commercial, industrial and corporate organisations based in Britain, including:

- public and private companies
- trade and professional associations
- educational and research establishments

The Awards, launched in 1984, are presented annually to individuals and groups who have significantly improved the standard of quality of a product, process or service. The Awards are open to any group or individual working in the United Kingdom. Each Award winner receives a trophy together with a certificate. The winners and those entries 'Highly Commended' may also use the BQA Award logo on printed and promotional material.

The judges look for:
A significant improvement in qualtiy in the last four years. This improvement to be in:

- product design and/or manufacture, or
- planning and/or operation of a service, or
- development and/or operation of a process

A process of continuous improvement, measured by some or all of the following:

- satisfying customers' requirements at a competitive cost
- motivation and education of personnel to improve quality standards
- better product or service performance
- technological innovation to improve quality standards
- quantifiable commercial and operational success
- a substantially higher standard than that prevalent in the relevant industrial sector, following the improvement in quality

In 1992 the Secretary of the Department of Trade and Industry announced that the government is leading an initiative for a new national award for quality in British business. The award will build on the work of the British Quality Association, include experience drawn from the Deming and Baldrige awards and also be compatible with The European Quality Award. A steering group of business leaders will pursue this initiative, being given the necessary staff and financial support from the Department of Trade and Industry.

11.5 THE EUROPEAN QUALITY AWARD

This award represents a fundamental shift in third party assessment awards, since, whilst there is still an emphasis on quality and systems, The European Quality Award incorporates a number of other areas.

The award sponsors are the European Commission, the European Foundation for Quality Management (EFQM) and the European Organisation for Quality. The EFQM has a membership of nearly 230 leading European businesses which all recognise the role of quality in achieving competitive advantage. The European Organisation for Quality was established in 1957 and has a federation of 25 national quality groups all with the aim of improving the quality and reliability of products and services.

The Award for 1992 incorporates:

The European Quality Prize, which will be awarded to a number of companies that demonstrate excellence in the management of quality as their fundamental process for continuous improvement, and *The European Quality Award*, which is awarded to the one most successful exponent of Total Quality Management in Western Europe. The trophy will be engraved and held nominally for one year by the recipient.

The award application document offers ideal guidelines against which performance can be benchmarked for self-appraisal. The criteria for assessment against the award are broken down into two sections. The **Results** criteria are concerned with *what* the company has achieved and is achieving. The **Enablers** are concerned with *how* results are being achieved. The **Enablers** are the means by which the company utilises its resources, including staff potential, and ensures that all processes are continuously reviewed and improved. The **Results** are those parameters that give a measurement of how well the **Enablers** are being utilised. To qualify for the award, measurement of results should ideally be demonstrated for the previous three or more years. The way that those outside, but with an interest in, the company, perceive the company's **Results** is also important. The company must be able to demonstrate not only the impact it has on its shareholders, but also on the local community. While it is appreciated that not everyone will currently be able to demonstrate compliance with the award requirements, it is hoped that by the year 2000, the requirements and standards for The 1992 European Quality Award will be the accepted norm.

Figure 11.1 shows the various sections under the two headings. Each of the nine sections is further subdivided into between four and six measurable areas.

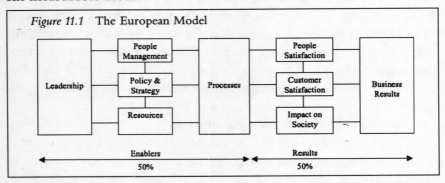

Figure 11.1 The European Model

Enablers

The following is an explanation of the various **Enablers** as they contribute to the European model for self-appraisal and in Figure 11.2, the criteria against which they will be scored is detailed.

1. Leadership

This accounts for 10 per cent of the points towards the Award.

The behaviour of all managers in driving the company towards total quality. How the executive team and all other managers inspire and drive total quality as the company's fundamental process for continuous improvement. Evidence is needed of:

1a Visible involvement in leading quality management
1b A consistent total quality culture
1c Recognition and appreciation of the efforts and successes of individuals and teams
1d Support of total quality by provision of appropriate resources and assistance
1e Involvement with customers and suppliers
1f The active promotion of quality management outside the company

2. Policy and Strategy

This accounts for 8 per cent of the points towards the Award.

The company's values, vision, and strategic direction – and the manner in which it achieves them.

How the company incorporates the concept of total quality in the determination, communication, implementation, review and improvement of its Policy and Strategy.

Evidence is needed of how policy and strategy are:

2a Based on the concept of total quality
2b Formed on the basis of information that is relevant to total quality
2c The basis for business plans
2d Communicated

Figure 11.2 Criteria for scoring *Enablers*

1) The degree of excellence of your *approach*
2) The degree of *deployment* of your approach

Approach / Deployment	%	Usage
Anecdotal or non value adding	0%	Little effective usage
Some evidence of soundly based approaches and prevention based systems. Subject to occasional review. Some area of integration into normal operations.	25%	Applied to about one quarter of the potential when considering all relevant areas and activities
Evidence of soundly based systematic approaches and prevention based systems. Subject to regular review with respect to business effectiveness. Integration into normal operations and planning well established.	50%	Applied to about half the potential when considering all relevant areas and activities.
Clear evidence of soundly based systematic approaches and prevention based systems. Clear evidence of refinement and improvement business effectiveness through review cycles. Good integration into normal operations and planning well established.	75%	Applied to about three quarters of the potential when considering all relevant areas and activities.
Clear evidence of soundly based systematic approaches and prevention based systems. Clear evidence of refinement and improvement business effectiveness through review cycles. Approach has become totally integrated into normal working patterns. Could be used as a role model for other organisations.	100%	Applied to full potential when considering all relevant areas and activities.

2e Regularly reviewed and improved

3. People and Management

This accounts for 9 per cent of the points towards the Award.

The management of the company's people.

How the company releases the full potential of its people to improve its business continuously. Evidence is needed on how:

3a Continuous improvement in People Management is effected
3b The company preserves and develops core skills through the recruitment, training and career progression of its people
3c The company's performance targets are agreed and are reviewed continuously with staff
3d The company promotes the involvement of all its people in continuous improvement and empowers its people to take appropriate action.

4. Resources

This accounts for 9 per cent of the points towards the Award.

The management, utilisation and preservation of resources.

Evidence is needed of how the company improves its business continuously, by optimisation of resources, based on the concept of total quality:

4a Financial resources
4b Information resources
4c Material resources
4d The application of technology

5. Processes

This accounts for 14 per cent of the points towards the Award.

The management of all the value-adding activities within the company.

How key and support processes are identified, reviewed and if necessary revised to ensure continuous improvement of the company's business.

Evidence is needed on:

5a How the key processes are identified

5b How the company systematically manages its key and support processes

5c How process performance parameters, along with all relevant feedback are used to review key processes and to set targets for improvement

5d How the company stimulates innovation and creativity in process improvement

5e How the company implements process changes and evaluates the benefits

Results

Just as **Enablers** are scored, **Results** can be similarly measured against the criteria given in Figure 11.3. For each of the four major **Results** headings, evidence is required for each of the following areas:

a Your company's own targets

b The relevance of parameters to all groups with an interest in the company

c Your company's actual performance

d The performance of competitors

e The performance of 'best in class' organizations

6. Customer Satisfaction

This accounts for 20 per cent of the points towards the Award.

What perception of your external customers, direct and indirect, is of the company and of its products and services.

Evidence is needed of the company's success in satisfying the needs and expectations of customers.

7. People Satisfaction

This accounts for 9 per cent of the points toward the Award.

What your people's feelings are about your company.

Evidence is needed of the company's success in satisfying the needs and expectations of its people.

Figure 11.3 Criteria for scoring *Results*

1) The degree of excellence of your *results* 2) The *scope* of your results		
Anecdotal	0%	Results address few relevant areas and activities
On balance a positive trend. Some satisfactory results.	25%	Results address some relevant areas and activities.
Strongly positive trend. Good results in most areas. Negative trends/results understood and have been addressed with well defined corrective/ prevention action plans.	50%	Results address many relevant areas and activities.
Strongly positive trend. Good results in most areas. Negative trends/results understood and have been addressed with well defined corrective/ prevention action plans.	75%	Results address most relevant areas and activities.
Excellent, "Best in class" results and strongly positive trends. Sustained performance. Positive indication that leading position will be maintained.	100%	Results address all relevant areas and facets of the organization.

8. Impact on Society

This accounts for 6 per cent of the points towards the Award.

What the perception of your company is among the community at large. This includes views of the company's approach to quality of life, the environment and to the preservation of global resources.

Evidence is needed of the company's success in satisfying the needs and expectations of the community at large.

9. Business Results

This accounts for 15 per cent of the points toward the Award.

What the company is achieving in relation to its planned business performance.

Evidence is needed of the company's continuing success in achieving its financial and other business targets and objectives, and in satisfying the needs and expectations of everyone with a financial interest in the company.

You must be able to demonstrate that your company's business plan is sound.

To be considered for these quality awards necessitates that companies re-evaluate all areas of their performance and not just concentrate on some quality aspects. Companies not only have to demonstrate their own internal quality improvements to:

> *product and service;*
> *processes;*
> *business;*

they must also be able to demonstrate that they have measures of:

> *their customers' satisfaction;*
> *their staff management;*

and now their impact on society and the environment.

12. A Case Study in Applying Measurement as Part of Total Quality Management – The Royal Mail

12.1 BACKGROUND

Royal Mail is one of the three main businesses of the Post Office Group and has a 350 year history. The Post Office has now made profits for 16 consecutive years and Royal Mail is by far the largest contributor, having made £266 million pre-tax in the year ending March 31st 1992. In the same year, some 61 million items of mail were handled daily – compared with 40 million a decade ago. Collections are made from more than 100,000 points every day and deliveries are made to all the UK's 24 million addresses. Royal Mail employs more than 170,000 people, is Europe's largest international mail carrier, and is second only to the USA in the handling of overseas mail.

As well as first and second class letter services, Royal Mail provides specialist services for major business mailers and priority and insured delivery services. In addition, it is a supplier to many millions of philatelists, both in the UK and abroad.

Customer First

Despite forecasts in the 1970s that the mail industry would decline in the face of pressure from the telephone, fax and electronic mail, postal mail volumes grew faster in the 1980s than in any other decade and Royal Mail, by now established as a separate business within the Post Office Group, operated profitably every year. However, there was some cause for concern. The growth in mail volumes was being achieved because the communications market was growing faster than the Royal Mail share was declining.

Furthermore, increased customer dissatisfaction was made evident by the level of complaints and negative press comment, and low employee morale was demonstrated by high staff turnover and industrial disputes, culminating in 1988 in the national postal strike. Also, although Royal Mail's front-line employees, the postmen and women, enjoyed the confidence of the public, this was not translated into a high regard for Royal Mail as a trusted supplier of services to businesses and the community as a whole.

Clearly, fundamental change was necessary. In early 1987, Bill Cockburn, Royal Mail Managing Director, decided to create the post of Quality Director within Royal Mail and in October of that year, Ian Raisbeck joined in that capacity. Ian Raisbeck had been a founder member of the Xerox Corporate Quality Office in Connecticut in the early 1980s and so was well-qualified to facilitate the introduction of Total Quality within Royal Mail.

Strong support for the new direction was given by Post Office Chairman Sir Bryan Nicholson. He had also taken up his post in October 1987 and, coincidentally, he had also experienced the basics of Total Quality at Xerox before establishing the Manpower Services Commission. It was decided that the achievements in terms of volume and profitability needed to be supplemented by a customer-focused Total Quality strategy if the long-term success of the business was to be secured. The strategy was named 'Customer First', indicating from the outset the basis on which it would operate.

12.2 Developing the Customer First Strategy

The first step in the change process was the agreement of the principles behind the Customer First direction for the business and central to the process was the involvement of employees from all areas of Royal Mail. In 1988, around 120 managers were brought together in small groups of six to define the current state of the business and the desired state for the future.

Several of the managers were initially reluctant to 'open up', believing that it was best to 'keep their heads down'. Eventually, a list of the shortcomings of the current situation was produced. Following further discussion, a list of requirements for the future was established:

- a well-structured product range based on market research of customer needs;
- effective *measurement* of customer satisfaction and a framework for acting upon it;
- understanding by employees and customers of all products and services;
- customer confidence generated by the presentation of a professional image in everything from uniforms and vans to enquiry offices;
- reliability in meeting the performance specifications of each product, based on the needs of customers, without failure.

Based on the outcome of these discussions, and reflecting the requirements of the four stakeholders (customers, employees, shareholders, community) the Royal Mail Business Mission was developed along with a statement of the values which the business holds, concerning the care of customers and employees. The Royal Mail Business Mission is shown in Figure 12.1, the Business Values are shown in Figure 12.2 and the Royal Mail definition of Total Quality is shown in Figures 12.3 and 12.4.

ROYAL MAIL BUSINESS MISSION

As Royal Mail our mission is to be recognised as the
best organisation in the world distributing text and packages
We shall achieve this by:

- Excelling in our Collection, Processing,
  Distribution and Delivery arrangements

- Establishing a partnership with our customers to
  understand, agree and meet their changing requirements

- Operating profitably by efficient services which
  our customers consider to be value for money

- Creating a work environment which recognises
  and rewards the commitment of all employees
  to customer satisfaction

- Recognising our responsibilities as part of the
  social, industrial and commercial life of the country

- Being forward looking and innovative

Figure 12.1   Royal Mail Business Mission

ROYAL MAIL BUSINESS VALUES

We each care about

- Our customers and their requirements for:
  - Reliability
  - Value for money
  - Accessibility
  - Courtesy
  - Integrity
  - Security
  - Prompt and timely response

- All our fellow employees and their needs for:
  - Respect
  - Training and development
  - Involvement
  - Recognition and reward

- The way we do our job and the way it affects our
  customers both inside and outside the Business

We are proud to be part of Royal Mail

Figure 12.2   Royal Mail Business Values

IN ROYAL MAIL "TOTAL QUALITY IS"

- A comprehensive way of working throughout the organisation which allows *all employees* as individuals and as teams to add value and *satisfy the needs of their customers*

- A business-wide customer driven strategy of change which moves us progressively to an environment where a *steady and continuous improvement of everything we do* is a way of life

Figure 12.3   Royal Mail Total Quality I

IN ROYAL MAIL "TOTAL QUALITY IS"

- Identifying and satisfying the needs of the customer starting with the external customer and working backwards so that *quality* at each step *is defined in terms of the "next customer"* in the process

- *Being both effective* (delivering the right products to the right segments of the market) *and efficient* (doing so at the most economical levels possible)

Figure 12.4   Royal Mail Total Quality II

Having established the aims of the business, the next task was to develop a strategy for achieving those aims. As a Total Quality process, emphasis was placed on team working, *measurement*, consistent improvement, the involvement of all functions, and the recognition of the chain of internal customers and suppliers which delivers the product to the end customer.

To create fundamental changes successfully in such a massive and widespread organisation, very careful, well informed and expertly directed planning was required.

To develop the strategy, all of the senior managers who reported to the Managing Director nominated a member of their own team to work with the Quality Director for three months. All functions were represented: operations, marketing, finance, personnel and sales.

Using the output from the earlier workshop sessions as a starting point, the Customer First team worked together for three days a week and then returned to their offices for the remainder of the week to test out the ideas that were being developed on their work colleagues.

The proposed Total Quality Process was incorporated into a five-year Business Plan with achievement milestones clearly defined for each year. The plan covered all of the aspects necessary to promote organisational change, cultural change and the use of *simple tools for measuring and improving quality*, with the collective aim of becoming a Total Quality Business, *as measured by increased customer satisfaction*. In essence, the change was to be from an organisation which had been control-oriented and internally-focused to one which is supportive and customer-focused.

The major components of the Total Quality Process for Royal Mail are illustrated in Figure 12.5, with the key factors that needed to be addressed shown at the ends of the ribs of the 'fishbone diagram'.

12.3 IMPLEMENTATION AND INVOLVEMENT

One of the key early decisions made when developing the implementation plan was that the process could not be rushed. The

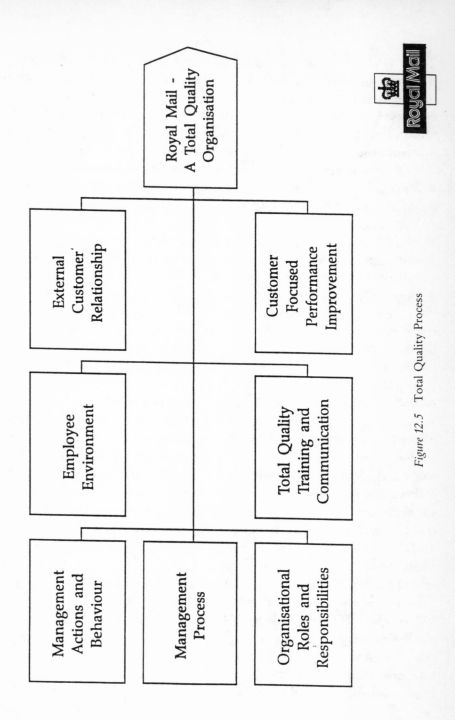

Figure 12.5 Total Quality Process

Total Quality process had to become part of the normal way of doing business – a way of life – and changes in attitude and policy had to become embedded before moving to the next step. Total Quality within Royal Mail had to be:

- substantive rather than cosmetic and focus on the improvement of cross-functional work processes and management processes;
- characterised by management leadership in building commitment, leading the implementation and providing positive role models, rather than sporadic exhortation;
- based on achieving effective implementation through the power of participation and supportive management actions rather than directions from above;
- carefully and systematically implemented taking into account the complexity of managing change in a large, people-dependent service organisation.

To achieve this, Customer First communication and training for managers was through a cascade based on work teams from the top of the organisation down. It began in January 1989 with a training workshop for Managing Director Bill Cockburn's team. The process of deploying the training throughout the organisation uses the 'Learn – Use – Lead – Support' cycle, whereby each manager learns the tools and techniques himself, uses them to carry out his own job, teaches them to his team of subordinates and then supports his subordinates as they themselves apply the lessons learned. The training is facilitated by Quality Support Managers who also work with the managers and teams on the improvement projects identified.

The Quality Support Managers act as agents for the change process and ensure that Customer First is implemented in line with the original direction identified. They report directly to senior managers and provide support in implementation planning, training, the identification and achievement of improvement opportunities and providing feedback. They also link together in networks to ensure consistency and share best practices.

Training modules were tailored for different areas of the business and a typical programme is illustrated in Figure 12.6. During the training sessions, which last five days, the trainees are encouraged to focus on what they and their teams do (their outputs) and how these could be improved. Frequently, at the start of the training sessions, some managers had difficulty in recognising their role in the customer–supplier chain and identified their outputs as the end product of the business – collecting and delivering letters – rather than their own specific contribution to the total process. At the end of the training they understood that the message was 'improve what you do'.

TRAINING AND COMMUNICATION

Content

Phase 1 *(1 day)*	Concepts of Quality
	Purpose and Output Definition
Phase 2 *(2 days)*	Improvement Process
	Analytical Tools/Techniques
Phase 3 *(2 days)*	Team Processes
	Management Actions and Behaviours
	Management of Improvement

Figure 12.6 Royal Mail Training Programme

By the end of 1989, all of the senior managers and a significant number of middle managers had received initial training and some improvement projects were under way. Awareness of the direction of Customer First and the concept of internal customers had been cascaded to all employees and an attitude survey had been carried out to establish a baseline. *Customer satisfaction parameters were also agreed and measured to determine the baseline.* External benchmarking commenced at the business and functional level.

By the end of 1990, the successes from initial improvement projects at national and local level had been communicated via various means, including special Teamwork events. These events are organised to allow project teams to show colleagues the improvement schemes they have generated and to share ideas and expertise. Some 75 per cent of the managers had now completed their training.

By the end of 1991, all managers had completed their initial training, and awareness training and improvement groups had been carried through to 2,500 front line employees in a pilot activity. In all, some 12,000 employees had been trained. Some 10 per cent of operational employees had participated in improvement projects and for the national Teamwork event, 100 teams came together, drawn from more than 50 local events all over the country. The improvement projects represented at the Teamwork exhibition included recruitment, training and aftercare of new postmen and women, stamp security, budgetary control, customer care and traffic tracking. One such improvement project case study from Teamwork '92 is described at the end of this chapter.

12.4 MEASURING FOR IMPROVEMENT

Alongside the process of informing and involving employees, the *measurement of performance, customer satisfaction and employee attitudes* has been crucial in the Customer First process and focus is given by *making comparisons with the best in the world.*

Delivery performance
As Royal Mail embarked on its Total Quality process, internal measurements of service indicated that performance of the basic first and second class letter service were at their highest levels, yet there

was clear customer dissatisfaction. Whilst internal measures showed that almost 90 per cent of first class mail was delivered the next day, surveys carried out by customer organisations indicated that only 70 per cent were meeting this standard.

An exact and independent measure of performance was needed before the right steps could be taken to improve the service provided to customers. The old system had monitored the time taken from when a postal item received the date stamp to when it was ready for delivery by the postman or woman. It took no account of problems at either end of the collection and delivery process, such as failure to clear a letter box or delivery to the wrong house.

In 1988, Royal Mail introduced an independently audited end-to-end measurement system – the first in the world. The system was approved by the statutory consumer watchdog, the Post Office Users' National Council (POUNC), was based on a sample of 250,000 letters annually and measured the time from 'pillar box to doormat'. The first results showed the performance for next-day delivery to be 74.5 per cent and not 90 per cent as had been believed!

To effect improvement, the results were analysed for each of the operational districts and then further broken down into local, medium and distant mail. *New improvement targets were set* for each of these three categories. Furthermore, *Quality of Service results became a key factor in determining senior management bonuses;* previously, bonuses were largely related to achievement of cost budgets. By 1991, the performance improved to 86 per cent delivered the next day, considerably better than the target agreed with POUNC. Figure 12.7 shows comparative reliability data and prices for Royal Mail and other European countries as established in a benchmarking exercise carried out by Research International. Royal Mail is the clear leader, both for delivery service and value for money. By March 1992, the next-day delivery figure had risen to 90 per cent. *The target is 95 per cent for 1995* and Royal Mail look well on the way to reaching it.

Customer satisfaction

Speed of delivery is not the only measurement used to assess the overall performance of the business. *A Customer Satisfaction Index was*

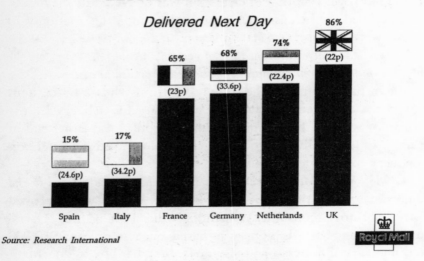

Figure 12.7 Letter Reliability 1991

introduced to assess how effectively Royal Mail deals with customer complaints. A sample of complainants are asked to give their views on how their complaints were handled. 'Mystery shopper' research is carried out through calls to Customer Care Units to measure attributes such as speed of response, knowledge and courtesy. *Feedback is provided to each of the Units who then use the findings to target areas for improvement.* A national customer care report is published to tabulate the results, highlight significant improvements and to exchange examples of best practice. In 1991, POUNC reported that the number of complaints about the first class mail service had dropped by 44 per cent and second class by 32 per cent.

The Customer Perception Index is another regular study that is used to focus improvement activities. This index measures performance of the service against priorities identified by customers themselves, such as the time of deliveries and condition in which the mail arrives. *Business and non-business customers, who have different sets of priorities, are researched separately* and examples of these measures for Brighton are shown in Figures 12.8 and 12.9.

CUSTOMER PERCEPTION INDEX

Business Customers (Brighton)

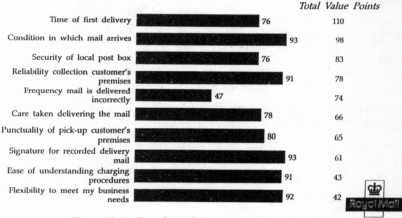

Figure 12.8   Royal Mail Customer Perception I

CUSTOMER PERCEPTION INDEX

Social Customers (Brighton)

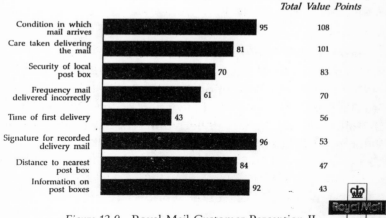

Figure 12.9   Royal Mail Customer Perception II

Opinion research that has been carried out shows marked improvements in public perception of the Royal Mail, and results from a number of recent surveys show that the public now rate Royal Mail more highly than any other major public utility service.

Employee attitudes

The final element is employee attitudes. It was established as a guiding principle of Customer First that *customer satisfaction and employee satisfaction are interdependent*. Attitude surveys are now carried out annually and published – warts and all – and data on employee satisfaction has also become an important factor in assessing managerial bonuses. Feedback is provided to managers on their behaviour by this group of internal 'customers' – namely the people who work for them. This feedback is amalgamated and used in a team discussion, involving the Quality Support Manager, to identify improvement opportunities. This often requires action by the team members as well as the manager.

Figure 12.10 shows some of the key measurements from the employee attitude survey used by Royal Mail and the improvements that have been recorded from the baseline established in 1989. Figure 12.11 illustrates sample questions from the management behaviour feedback system and Figure 12.12 shows the rating categories used when answering the questions.

Benchmarking with quality leaders

In October 1990, Royal Mail was represented among a party of 15 Post Office Directors and senior managers who undertook a study tour to the USA. The tour visited winners of the Malcolm Baldrige Award, all of whom operate in very different market environments and offer a different approach to Total Quality.

The companies visited were:

- Milliken Industries – one of the world's largest textile companies
- IBM – the information technology giant
- Motorola Inc. – the leading manufacturer of electronic

EMPLOYEE ATTITUDE SURVEY

Key Measurements 1990 – 91

Satisfaction with Communications *(% very/fairly satisfied)*	*1989*	*1990*	*1991*
Managers	42%	49%	57.5%
Non Managers	36%	42.8%	49%

Royal Mail Recognises Good Work *(% agreeing strongly/slightly)*			
Managers	22%	35%	56.8%
Non Managers	12%	25%	36.7%

Royal Mail Believes Employees Important *(% agreeing strongly/slightly)*			
Managers	26%	46%	52.2%
Non Managers	14%	32%	35.9%

Figure 12.10   Royal Mail Employee Attitude Survey

MANAGEMENT BEHAVIOUR FEEDBACK SYSTEM

Sample Questions

In working with members of my team I:

- Provide them with honest and practical feedback   A   B   C1   C2   D
  on their job performance

- Gain input from team members before making   A   B   C1   C2   D
  decisions affecting our area

- Demonstrate respect for others in the   A   B   C1   C2   D
  organisation

- Encourage them to work as a team through my   A   B   C1   C2   D
  personal involvement

- Strive to remove barriers which inhibit efficiency   A   B   C1   C2   D
  and effectiveness

- Set objectives based on customer requirements   A   B   C1   C2   D

Figure 12.11   Royal Mail Management Behaviour Feedback System

MANAGEMENT BEHAVIOUR FEEDBACK SYSTEM

Rating Categories

A	Frequency very low
B	Frequency below requirement Effectiveness below requirement
C1	Frequency below requirement Effectiveness meets requirement
C2	Frequency meets requirement Effectiveness below requirement
D	Frequency meets requirement Effectiveness meets requirement

Figure 12.12   Royal Mail Management Behaviour Feedback System

equipment systems and components
- Westinghouse Electric Corporation – whose enterprises cover a range as diverse as radar technology, nuclear power and domestic appliances

Each of the companies has been recognised as a leader in a particular area of the Total Quality approach: Milliken were asked to discuss in detail their people development, IBM their business-wide process improvements, Motorola focused on reduction in error levels and Westinghouse described their quality reviews and overall integrated approach. All of the companies are a decade along the Total Quality route, and the information shared allowed the Royal Mail team to confirm that their initial steps were on the right track. Further, though, it provided concepts and techniques that could be adapted and adopted by Royal Mail itself to develop further plans for action. Such study tours are now a regular annual event. It is also significant that at the time of writing, senior executives from the US Post Service are in the UK (Midlands and Scotland) to benchmark their performances against Royal Mail at a national and local level.

12.5 TAKING ACTION

Armed with data from the diverse measurement systems within the business, and using information from the benchmarking exercise mentioned above, Royal Mail have taken action across the business.

Operational

The new analyses of delivery service, broken down by district and distance of delivery, allowed for better diagnoses of the problems and remedial testing. Operational improvements included the switching of local and medium distance mail traffic from rail to road. The new road links meant that mail arrived at key sorting offices up to three hours earlier. All weekend mail was also switched to road. Long distance trunking and the sorting of mail on the move remained with the railways, for which it is best suited.

Far greater use is also being made of air transport and, by 1991, one in seven first class letters was travelling by air. New airlinks from the South coast and South West to the North East, Scotland, East Anglia and the North West were introduced and a new weekend air network established. In addition, the Sunday collection of mail, stopped since 1976, was reintroduced from 20,000 pillar boxes in both urban and rural areas, leading to millions more letters arriving on Monday morning.

Further, the business embarked on a rolling programme of investment in the latest sorting technology: machinery to turn envelopes face upwards, cancel the stamps and separate first and second class; optical character recognition machines which read the phosphor code automatically; high speed sorting equipment. A new computer system was developed and is being introduced to plan the most efficient collection and delivery routes; already savings of up to 20 per cent in total urban mileage are being seen.

For employees

Beside the operational changes, improvements have been made with respect to employee relations and involvement. The improvement in the attitude survey results have already been mentioned.

Following the 1988 postal strike, the prospects of involving all employees in the Total Quality process – an essential requirement – may have looked bleak. However, a step-by-step approach was adopted. With front-line employees – the postmen and women, sorters and drivers – emphasis was placed on demonstrating in tangible ways the business's concern for their welfare and the recognition of their roles as ambassadors for Royal Mail. This has included better provision in basic issues such as the supply of uniforms and footwear. A leisure magazine, published every two months, is circulated to 350,000 existing and retired staff and capitalises on Royal Mail's considerable buying power to offer products at discounted prices.

Recognition of the contributions that employees have made has led to the introduction of a number of schemes, including long-service awards. Further opportunities are presented through involvement in project teams. The teamwork philosophy has been embraced by employees from all disciplines and all levels: caterers, secretaries and engineers as well as postal and managerial staff. The events, organised locally and nationally to recognise and applaud the commitment shown, have already been mentioned.

Developments include pre-recruitment training, targets for the employment of under-represented groups and the revision of promotion procedures. Career breaks and job-sharing have been introduced to help retain experienced staff and Royal Mail has taken a leading role in setting up 'Opportunity 2000', a major equal-opportunities drive to increase the representation of women at all levels throughout British industry. Training is seen to be crucial and managers and postal staff are encouraged to develop their skills by taking various training options made available.

For customers

Business customers are beginning to recognise the improvements within Royal Mail's activities. Part of Royal Mail's policy is to develop business partnerships with major customers, one of which is Kodak Ltd. Kodak, in Hemel Hempstead, posts more than two million items a year and teams from both businesses meet regularly to discuss the maintenance and improvement of quality of service. As a result of this partnership, Kodak awarded a Quality First certificate to Royal Mail Oxford. Similar partnerships are being forged with other major customers, and relationships are being fostered with trade associations and mail user conferences with a view to consulting on, and trialling, new services.

Royal Mail is also concerned to make itself much more accessible to its customers when they need information, or when they have a problem. Name badges have been introduced for all staff in direct contact with the public, unless there are issues of personal safety, and staff give their names on the telephone and in correspondence. The details of the nearest Customer Care Office is shown on each of the 100,000 pillar boxes and in the windows of main post offices. There are published standards for dealing with enquiries or complaints – an acknowledgement issued on the day of receipt and a detailed reply within ten working days. Every address also receives information, including local performance, in the Post Guide.

Restructuring the business

In April 1992, the old Royal Mail structure of 64 districts was replaced by one based around the 120 postcode areas with four Strategic Business Units focusing on different market segments. The aims of the new de-centralised structure are to move closer to both the general public and the business customer in the provision of services, to encourage the development of products to meet specific needs, to cut bureaucracy and to establish a management process which provides for full participation in the development and implementation of strategies. Staff at the central headquarters in London have been slimmed down from 2,000 to 170, with many being transferred to other areas of the business. It has also meant the removal of three management layers between the Managing Director and front-line employees.

The postcode areas are now organised within nine new Divisions, each a sizeable business in its own right with, on average, a £300 million turnover, 20,000 staff, 150 delivery offices, 200 buildings, 55,000 business customers and six million non-business customers. Within each Division, accountability for customer satisfaction, end-to-end performance and employee satisfaction will be further devolved to managers covering postcode areas. *The publication of performance results for each of the 120 postcode areas will extend the benefits of the measurement system*, both for the business, which will continue to be able to use the data diagnostically, and for customers – who will see clearly the performance of the mail service in their area. Figure 12.13 illustrates the performance measures at Divisional level.

MEASUREMENT OF PERFORMANCE

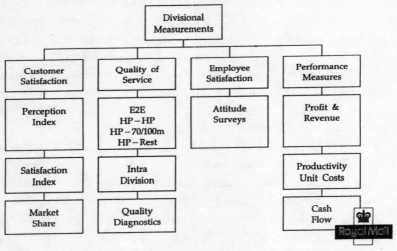

Figure 12.13 Divisional Performance Measurement

The four Strategic Business Units are also responsible for their own management and profitability and for targeting their products and services at particular areas of the overall market: Royal Mail Streamline focuses on large business mailers; Royal Mail International, on the international market; Royal Mail National caters for philatelic, individuals, small businesses and priority service customers; Royal Mail Cashco offers a high-value package-distribution operation.

The strategic management direction of the business is now defined by five Steering Groups, each led by the appropriate director from the senior team of Royal Mail. The five strategic areas relate to customers, employees, operational processes, profitability and Total Quality and the agreed strategic direction is deployed to line-management for operational implementation. The Steering Groups are supported by long-term Focus Groups and Improvement Teams, created to address specific opportunities. Membership of the groups is primarily from the Divisions and Business Units and is based on ability to contribute rather than rank (See Figure 12.14).

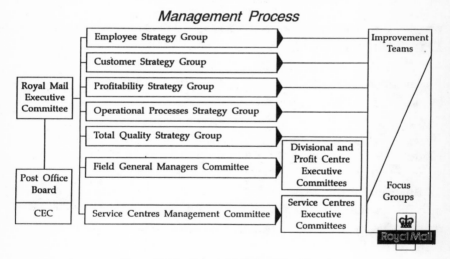

Figure 12.14 Royal Mail Steering Groups

12.6 The future

Despite the improvements made, Royal Mail considers that, compared to the companies benchmarked in America, their Total Quality process is still at a comparatively early stage. However, the direction set in 1988 has encouraged teamwork and involvement, and there has been measurable progress in many key areas.

In the next phase, emphasis will be placed on further definition and improvement of the business processes that drive Royal Mail. Individuals and teams will continue to improve what they do, but in the context of understanding their part in the overall process and also how their work has an impact in a positive sense on the external customer.

Customer First is a continuing cycle of research, innovation, improvement and review, *with measurement providing the data for each of these steps,* in a process which will continue until Royal Mail achieves its mission of being recognised as the best in the world.

12.7 TEAMWORK AT THE HODDESDON DELIVERY OFFICE

As an illustration of the above approach, a brief case study at the Hoddesdon Delivery Office follows.

Background

Hoddesdon is a town in the Enfield district, some 20 miles north of London, post code area EN11. There are 13,600 delivery points or destinations in the 24 square mile area and these are broken down into 38 separate delivery rounds. About 28,000 items are delivered daily. The team of 53 postal staff and one manager are also responsible for making collections from 38 post boxes.

Mail for the Hoddesdon area is delivered to the office where it is sorted by the postmen and women in a two–stage operation. The first stage consists of sorting into the 38 delivery areas; the second stage involves further sorting each delivery into the order that the postman or woman will actually deliver the mail. Sorting is done by the use of 30 frames, each containing 48 'pigeon holes'. Of the 38 delivery groupings, six are for companies and 32 are for private addresses – houses. The remaining 'pigeon holes' are used for 'specials' of one type or another.

Getting started

The improvement project concerns deliveries made by the 32 walks covering residential deliveries.

Owing to growth and new developments in the Hoddesdon area over the previous decade, deliveries had increased and mis-sorted letters had risen in step. The mis-sorts being considered occur at the first sorting stage and are identified at phase two. They obviously involve having to do the work again, cause time-wasting delays and frustration, and could lead to dissatisfied customers. Despite various changes to the sorting system, the rate of mis-sorts remained unacceptably high at 4.6 per cent.

To tackle the problem, Martin Bates, the Office Manager, enlisted the help of George Rendall, the Quality Support Manager from Royal Mail London who had been the facilitator during Martin's initial Customer First training. A team including Martin and four volunteers from the postal staff was set up and began by considering the best way to approach the problem. The other team members were:

Barbara Bidwell – Postwoman;
Bill Clements – Postman;
Chris House – Postman;
Tim Wing – Postman.

A fact-finding exercise was started, to measure where the main problem areas lay. To collect the data, all of the postal staff were asked to record the number of wrongly sorted letters, which round they should have been for, and to which round they had been designated.

In addition, individual members of staff we... their accuracy of sorting performance and tc specific problems. Initially, the data collection with paper and pencil, but the acquisition of a allowed the team to build a database of relev display it easily as bar charts and graphs.

When the data were analysed, seven out (

were shown to receive a higher proportion of mis-sorts than the remainder. Other issues were highlighted by the analysis and ideas on likely causes were put forward during team brainstorming sessions:

- Roads with the same name, i.e. Priory Close, Hoddesdon and Priory Close, Turnford
- Individually named properties, which are vague addresses
- New roads and housing estates
- New starters who live outside the Hoddesdon delivery area and do not know where all the addresses are
- Newer members of staff who have not been given the opportunity to become familiar with all of the rounds
- People who limit their learning opportunities by doing little or no overtime to cover others' rounds
- Older, longer-serving staff still sorting to original sortation and ignoring the changes made to cope with growth, e.g. splitting rounds
- There had been a lack of continuity of management which led to a dilution of the delivery area knowledge available to help others

Finding a cure

Once the causes of the problem were understood, the team put forward ideas to remedy them; most have already been implemented:

- Information boards for each delivery walk above the frames were fully updated and a 'hazard address' column was added to highlight those addresses with a high mis-sort probability
- Small stickers were placed on the inside of frame selections for difficult rounds, giving added information
- A pack of 120 training cards (dummy letters) was introduced covering all roads that are split across two rounds, to be used for new recruits and as part of continuous training exercises
- A further pack of 300 training cards was introduced with the most awkward addresses, e.g. house names, new housing estates

- Local maps were coloured in sections to highlight problem roads and new developments
- The suggestion to rotate duties rather than keep them fixed is under review.

Result

As a result of measuring the causes of mis-sorts and taking action on the findings, the mis-sort rate has been reduced from 4.6 per cent to 1.9 per cent. The Hoddesdon team, and indeed all in the Delivery Office, should be proud of the improvements they have made and deserved the recognition they received at the Teamwork '92 event.

13. Doing It UK

Now that you have read this book you will appreciate that measurement of quality is an important step along the road to continuous improvement. This section, and the checklists and details included here, will facilitate the application of quality, and its measurement, within your organisation.

Use this section as a focusing tool individually, compare the results with colleagues, or send them in for us to analyse.

I. Relationships of Mission Statement to Measurable Critical Success Factors

Mission/Vision Statement:

Has this been derived from a Senior Management workshop?

☐☐
Yes No

Has it been examined for completeness?

☐☐
Yes No

Has it been communicated to all staff?

☐☐
Yes No

Have Critical Success Factors been identified?

☐☐
Yes No

Are these derived directly from the Mission Statement?

☐☐
Yes No

Critical Success Factors

Complete the following table, specifying your organisation's Critical Success Factors and their implementation:

Critical Success Factor (CSF)	Measurable?	Is a target set?	Is it realistic?	Who is responsible for achieving it?
1				
2				
3				
4				
5				
6				
7				

2. TARGETS

For each of your organisation's Critical Success Factors specify targets to be reached after 6, 12, 24, 36 and 60 months or other appropriate periods.

Critical Success Factor	6 months?	12 months?	24 months?	36 months?	60 months?
1					
2					
3					
4					
5					
6					
7					

How do you select targets? ....
Are they achievable?.................... How do you know? ....
....
Is there a better way? ....

3. CURRENT PERFORMANCE AND IMPROVEMENT ACTIVITY

Critical Success Factor	Current Level/ Performance	Improvement Action Plan	Who is Responsible
1			
2			
3			
4			
5			
6			
7			

4. COST OF QUALITY

What is your Cost of Quality as a percentage of Turnover/Sales?...

....

How do you know?..

How do you measure it? ....

What is excluded? ....

What is included? ....

How is it changing over time? ....

Please specify your major Quality Cost headings and how much they represent two years ago, today, and in 12 months' time.

Cost £		24 months ago	12 months ago	6 months ago	Now	Prediction 6 months time	12 months time
Major	1						
	2						
Quality	3						
	4						
Cost	5						
Headings	6						
	7						
Target, if aplicable							

5. USE OF MEASUREMENT AND MONITORING TOOLS

Tools	Areas being used	Areas could be applied to	Why is it not being applied?	How should we approach Implementation?
1 Tools of Quality Control				
2 Pareto charts	....	....	....	....
3 Cause & effect diagrams	....	....	....	....
4 Stratification	....	....	....	....
5 Check sheets	....	....	....	....
6 Histograms	....	....	....	....
7 Scatter diagrams	....	....	....	....
8 Control charts	....	....	....	....
9 Run charts				
10 SPC				
11 Taguchi Methodology				
12 QFD				
13 Process Deployment Flow Charts				
14 Cost of Quality				
15 Critical Success Factors				
16 Benchmarking				
17				
18				
19				
20				

6. Approach to Measuring and Monitoring

Use

Do all staff use measurement and monitoring
techniques?

Yes No

Who uses them?..

For what processes/activities? ....

Specialists

What specialist groups undertaking measurements and monitoring
exist?..
....
How integrated are these groups into the organisation? ....
....
Are there any communication problems? ....
....

Training

What training in measurement and monitoring techniques is carried
out?...
....
....
Who receives training? ....
How is training carried out? ....
....
What is the focus of the training?..
....

Coherence

How is measurement and monitoring used?..................................
....
Is it a coherent programme or isolated uses?

Coherent Isolated

Specify any difficulties with measurement....................................
....
....

Measurement
Is measurement of outputs, inputs or the process
(or any 2 or 3)?

Outputs	Inputs	Process

To what is output measurement applied? ....
....
....

To what is input measurement applied? ....
....
....

To what is process measurement applied? ....
....
....

Where could further process measurement be introduced?..............
....
....

Feedback
Is measurement used for feedback and change?

Yes	No

If yes, where? ....
....

Where not? ....
....

Where could Feedback be introduced?...
....

Timescale
Is measurement current or historic?

Current	Historic

Examples...
....
....

Where could further current measurement be utilised? ....
....
....

Is measurement directly related to customer requirements or to internal requirements?

Customer	Internal

Where could further relationships to customer requirements be introduced?...

....

Stakeholders

What measurement/monitoring exists related to other Stakeholders in your organisation (i.e. not customers)?...............................

....

....

Specify your Stakeholders and the Critical Success Factors that relate to them:

Stakeholder	CSF	Is it Measurable?	Is a Target set?
1			
2			
3			
4			
5			
6			
7			

7. PROCESSES

Have you defined your core business processes?

Yes	No

Are all stages listed, together with inputs, outputs, process owners and measurement points for each?

Yes	No

What do you measure for each process?

Core Process	Stages	Measurement Points	Process Owner
1			
2			
3			
4			
5			
6			
7			

How do you set targets? ....
....
....
....

Draw one of your core business processes using a process Deployment Flowchart:

"Cast of characters"							

How does your organisation know what matters to the customer and their relative importance? ....
....
....

How do you know your organisation's performance in terms of these wants, and how do they compare to those of your competitors?
....
....

Specify measurement points and methods for this activity. ....
....
....

Generalise this approach to all your personal core activities:

	Core Activity	Stages	Measurement		Target (with date)
			Points	Methods	
1.		1._____ 2._____ 3._____ 4._____			
2.		1._____ 2._____ 3._____ 4._____			
3.		1._____ 2._____ 3._____ 4._____			
4.		1._____ 2._____ 3._____ 4._____			

Define your Personal Quality monitoring system ....
....
....

Define your Personal Quality Remedial Actions ....
....
....

8. Voice of the Customer

Does your organisation listen to the "Voice of the Customer?"

Yes	No

How is it obtained? _____
_____

How should it be obtained? _____
_____

Construct a "House of Quality" for one of your organisation's products or services.

Step 2
Enter Here
the operating
requirements to
help achieve
customer wants

Step 4
Here
try to
benchmark
against your
competitors on
a 1-5 scale

Operating
Requirements

Importance to customer

Customer
Requirements

								1	2	3	4	5
	1											
	2											
	3											
	4											
	5											

Step 1
Enter here
what matters to the
customer and their
relative importance
1-5 (5 is most
important)

Step 3
Enter in
body of table the
connections between
what matters to the
customer and
business processes

9. Personal Quality

How do you measure yourself? _____
_____
_____

Do you set yourself targets? _____
_____
_____

Select one of your core activities, define the stages of the activity and inputs and outputs
and draw/chart it below:-

10 BENCHMARKING

What processes for making comparisons with other organisations do you have in place?...
....
....

How do you obtain relevant data? ....
....
....

Specify below possible measurements within your organisation that could be the basis for benchmarking:

Measure	Current perform-ance	Physical Limit (if applicable)	Competitors Performance			"World's Best Practice"	Target /Date	How to Close the Gap
			A	B	C			
1								
2								
3								
4								
5								
6								
7								
8								
9								
10								

THIS PAGE WILL ONLY BE OF RELEVANCE IF YOU WISH TO RETURN A COPY OF THESE CHECKLISTS TO US FOR ANALYSIS

Total number of employees..

Number of site
and locations...

Nature of Core Business...

Turnover..

Is the organisation undertaking a TQM programme?   ☐ ☐

                                                  Yes No

If yes, how long has this been under way?.......................

Details for Correspondence (Details of individual completing the form or collating replies)

Name... Post ....

Telephone No. .... Extension.....................

Company ....

Address ....

....

....

Fax No. ....

What to do Now

If you have completed the previous pages, or have at least attempted to, the next steps for you or your organisation may already be clear to you and your colleagues.

However, should your responses have provoked additional questions, or you are not clear how to proceed further, you are welcome to photocopy the pages and send them to us, in strictest confidence, outlining your problem and we will supply *free of charge* the guidance which seems appropriate.

We also gain, since the more we know, the more we understand. Your views on our book are also most welcome!

The Authors
c/o Services Ltd.
Quality & Reliability House
82 Trent Boulevard
West Bridgford
Nottingham NG2 5BL

Tel. 0602–455285
Fax. 0602–817137

BIBLIOGRAPHY

Books

Bassert J.L. *Quality Function Deployment – A Practioner's Approach*, Milwaukee: ASQC Quality Press/Marcel Dekker (1991)

Bendell A., Wilson G., Millar R.M.G. *Taguchi Methodology Within Total Quality*, Bedford: IFS Publications (1990)

Bendell A. *The Quality Gurus: What can they do for your Company?*, DTI (1992)

Bendell A., Disney J., Pridmore W.A. (ed) *Taguchi Methods: Applications in World Industry*, Bedford, IFS Publications (1989)

Camp R.C. *Benchmarking: The Search for Industry Best Practices that Lead to Superior Performance*, Milwaukee: ASQC Quality Press (1989)

Deming W.E. *Out of the Crisis*, Cambridge: Cambridge University Press (1986)

Feigenbaum A.V. *Total Quality Control*, Maidenhead: McGraw-Hill (1991)

Hudiburg J.J. *Winning with Quality*, New York: Quality Resources (1991)

Ishikawa K. *What is Total Quality Control? The Japanese Way*, London: Prentice Hall (1985)

Ishikawa K. *Guide to Quality Control*, Tokyo: Asian Productivity Organisation (1976)

Juran J.M. et al (ed) *Quality Control Handbook*, New York: McGraw-Hill (1988)

Juran J.M. *Juran on Planning for Quality*, New York: The Free Press (1988)

Mann N.R. *The Keys to Excellence: The Story of the Deming Philosophy*, London: Mercury (1989)

Møller C. *Personal Quality*, Denmark: Time Manager International A/S (1987)

Neave H.R. *The Deming Dimension*, Knoxville: SPC Press (1990)

Oakland J.S. *Statistical Process Control*, London: William Heinemann (1986)

Owen M. *SPC and Continuous Improvement*, Bedford: IFS Publications/Berlin: Springer-Verlag (1989)

Shewhart W. *Economic Control of Quality of Manufactured Product*, New York: Van Nostrand (1931)

Shingo S. *Zero Quality Control: Source Inspection and the Poka-yoke System*, Cambridge Ma: Productivity Press (1986)

Taylor F.W. *Principles of Scientific Management*, New York: Harper and Row (1915)

Proceedings of the East Midlands Quality Club World Quality Day Conference '*Quality Brings Success*', 1991

Best Practice Benchmarking, DTI, 1992

Video Training Course
The TQM Video Series (Module 1: The Quality Gurus and Total Quality Management, Module 2: The Tools of Total Quality Management, Module 3: Implementing Total Quality and ISO 9000), 1992. Available from Services Ltd, Quality & Reliability House, 82 Trent Boulevard, West Bridgford, Nottingham, NG2 5BL. (Tel. 0602 455285, Fax 0602 817137).

Index